The Suppor[illegible] Guide to Premier & Football League Clubs 2010

EDITOR
John Robinson

Twenty-sixth Edition

CONTENTS

British Library Cataloguing in Publication Data
A catalogue record for this book is available from the British Library

ISBN: 978-1-86223-182-5

72 St. Peter's Avenue, Cleethorpes, N.E. Lincolnshire, DN35 8HU, England
Web site http://www.soccer-books.co.uk
e-mail info@soccer-books.co.uk

Manufactured in the UK by LPPS Ltd, Wellingborough, NN8 3PJ

FOREWORD

These are critical times for many clubs particularly those facing points penalties before the season commences and we are indebted to the staffs of all the clubs featured in this guide for their cooperation and also to Michael Robinson (page layouts), Bob Budd (cover artwork) and Tony Brown (Cup Statistics – www.soccerdata.com).

When using this guide, please note that 'child' concessions also include senior citizens unless stated otherwise. Some clubs had not fixed their matchday admission prices at the time of going to press and in these cases we have had to use the 2008/2009 prices in the absence of new information. It should be noted that although actual matchday admission prices are shown in this guide, many clubs offer discounts for tickets purchased before the day of the game.

Disabled Supporters' information is once again included in the guide and, to ensure that facilities are not overstretched, we recommend that disabled fans pre-book wherever possible.

Regular purchasers of the guide will notice that we have included a number of new ground photographs in this edition. Ground moves and redevelopment are continuing apace and travelling fans may find that away sections and prices change during the course of the 2009/2010 season. If the Government's planned increase in VAT goes back up to 17½% in December 2009, matchday admission prices will, of necessity, increase.

If any readers have alternative ground photos which they would like us to consider for insertion in future issues, they should write to me care of the address opposite.

Finally, we would like to wish our readers a happy and safe spectating season.

John Robinson

John Robinson
EDITOR

WEMBLEY STADIUM

First Opened: 1923 (Re-opened in 2007 after rebuild)
Address: Wembley National Stadium, Wembley, London HA9 0WS
Correspondence: P.O.Box 1966, London, SW1P 3EQ
Telephone Nº: 0844 980-8001
Fax Number: (020) 8795-5050
Seating Capacity: 90,000 over three tiers –
Lower Tier: 34,303 seats
Middle Tier: 16,532 seats
Upper Tier: 39,165 seats
Web site: www.wembleystadium.com

GENERAL INFORMATION

Car Parking: The stadium is a Public Transport Location and, as such, parking is only available for pre-accredited vehicles. Any spaces which are available must be pre-purchased from the following web site: www.csparking.com/stadium
Coach Travel: National Express operates 13 coach routes from 43 major towns and cities direct to the stadium for special events: www.nationalexpress.com/wembley
Rail & Tube Travel: Wembley Park station is on the Jubilee and Metropolitan tube lines; Wembley Stadium station is on the Bakerloo tube line and the Silver Link train line; Wembley Central station is on the Chiltern train line which runs from Marylebone Station
Local Bus Services: Services 18, 83, 92, 182 and 224 all travel to the stadium

DISABLED INFORMATION

Wheelchairs: 310 spaces for wheelchairs are available in total alongside 310 seats for helpers. A further 100 enhanced amenity seats are available for ambulant disabled visitors.
Disabled Toilets: Disabled toilets are available throughout the stadium.

ACCRINGTON STANLEY FC

Founded: 1876 (Reformed 1968)
Former Names: None
Nickname: 'Stanley' 'Reds'
Ground: The Fraser Eagle Stadium, Livingstone Road, Accrington, Lancashire BB5 5BX
Record Attendance: 4,368 (3rd January 2004)
Pitch Size: 112 × 72 yards

Colours: Red shirts and shorts
Telephone Nº: 0871 434-1968
Fax Number: (01254) 356951
Ground Capacity: 5,057
Seating Capacity: 1,200
Web site: www.accringtonstanley.co.uk

GENERAL INFORMATION

Supporters Club: Malcolm Isherwood, c/o Club
Telephone Nº: –
Car Parking: 300 spaces available at the ground
Coach Parking: At the ground
Nearest Railway Station: Accrington (1 mile)
Nearest Bus Station: Accrington Town Centre (1 mile)
Club Shop: At the ground, at Oswaldtwistle Mills Shopping Village and also through the club web site
Opening Times: Weekdays 9.00am – 5.00pm; Saturday matchdays 10.00am – 5.00pm
Telephone Nº: (01254) 356954
Police Telephone Nº: (01254) 382141

GROUND INFORMATION

Away Supporters' Entrances & Sections: Signposted on matchdays

ADMISSION INFO (2009/2010 PRICES)

Adult Standing: £13.00
Adult Seating: £15.00
Senior Citizen Standing: £8.00
Senior Citizen Seating: £10.00
Ages 12-16 Standing: £4.00
Ages 12-16 Seating: £5.00
Under-12s Standing/Seating: £1.00
Programme Price: £2.50

DISABLED INFORMATION

Wheelchairs: Specific areas around the ground
Helpers: Admitted
Prices: Concessionary prices are charged for the disabled. Helpers are admitted free of charge
Disabled Toilets: Available
Contact: (01254) 356950 Michael Schultz, Disabled Liaison Officer (Bookings are not necessary)

Travelling Supporters' Information:
Routes: Take the M6 to the M65 signposted for Blackburn/Burnley. Exit at Junction 7 and follow the sign for Padiham. Turn right at first traffic lights then right at next. Follow Whalley Road towards Accrington, go through lights at the Greyhound Inn. Turn left into Livingstone Road, 500 yards past traffic lights (signposted Accrington Stanley). The ground is signposted from Junction 7 of the M65 – follow the brown signs with the white football.

ALDERSHOT TOWN FC

Founded: 1992 (Entered League: 2008)
Former Names: Aldershot FC
Nickname: 'Shots'
Ground: EBB Stadium, Recreation Ground, High Street, Aldershot GU11 1TW
Record Attendance: 7,500 (18th November 2000)
Pitch Size: 117 × 76 yards

Colours: Red shirts with Blue trim, Red shorts
Telephone Nº: (01252) 320211
Fax Number: (01252) 324347
Club Secretary: (01252) 320211– Graham Hortop
Ground Capacity: 7,100
Seating Capacity: 1,879
Web site: www.theshots.co.uk

GENERAL INFORMATION

Supporters Club: c/o Club
Telephone Nº: (01252) 320211
Car Parking: Municipal Car Park is adjacent
Coach Parking: Contact the club for information
Nearest Railway Station: Aldershot (5 mins. walk)
Nearest Bus Station: Aldershot (5 minutes walk)
Club Shop: At the ground
Opening Times: Matchdays only
Telephone Nº: (01252) 320211
Police Telephone Nº: (01252) 324545

GROUND INFORMATION

Away Supporters' Entrances & Sections:
Accommodation in the East Bank Terrace, Bill Warren section (South Stand) – Redan Hill Turnstiles Nº 11 and 12.

ADMISSION INFO (2009/2010 PRICES)

Adult Standing: £15.00
Adult Seating: £18.00
Under-18s Standing: £9.00 (Under-16s: £5.00)
Under-18s Seating: £10.00 (Under-16s: £6.00)
Senior Citizen Standing: £12.00
Senior Citizen Seating: £13.00
Programme Price: £3.00

DISABLED INFORMATION

Wheelchairs: Accommodated in the North Stand
Helpers: Admitted
Prices: Free of charge for the disabled and helpers
Disabled Toilets: Available
Contact: (01252) 320211 (Bookings are helpful)

Travelling Supporters' Information:
Routes: From the M3: Exit at Junction 4 and follow signs for Aldershot (A331). Leave the A331 at the A323 exit (Ash Road) and continue along into the High Street. The ground is just past the Railway Bridge on the right; From the A31: Continue along the A31 to the junction with the A331, then as above; From the A325 (Farnborough Road): Follow signs to the A323 then turn left into Wellington Avenue. The ground is just off the 2nd roundabout on the left – the floodlights are clearly visible.

ARSENAL FC

Founded: 1886 (**Entered League:** 1893)
Former Names: Royal Arsenal (1886-1891) and Woolwich Arsenal (1891-1914)
Nickname: 'Gunners'
Ground: Emirates Stadium, Drayton Park N5
Ground Capacity: 60,335 (All seats)
Pitch Size: 110 × 71 yards
Record Attendance: 60,161 (3rd November 2007)

Colours: Red shirts with White sleeves, White shorts
Telephone N°: (020) 7619-5000
Ticket Office: 0844 277-3625
Fax Number: (020) 7704-4041
Web Site: www.arsenal.com

GENERAL INFORMATION

Car Parking: None
Coach Parking: Visit the web site for further details
Nearest Railway Station: Finsbury Park and Highbury & Islington
Nearest Tube Station: Arsenal (Piccadilly), Finsbury Park, Highbury & Islington and Holloway Road are all nearby
Club Shop: At the ground and at Finsbury Park Tube Station
Opening Times: Monday to Saturday 9.00am to 5.00pm; Sundays 10.00am to 4.00pm
Telephone N°: (020) 7619-5000
Police Telephone N°: (020) 7263-9090

GROUND INFORMATION

Away Supporters' Entrances & Sections:
Green quadrant – follow colour coding system at the ground

ADMISSION INFO (2009/2010 PRICES)

Adult Seating: £32.50 – £92.00
Child Seating: £13.00 – £18.00 (In the Family Enclosure)
Senior Citizen Seating: £14.00 – £20.00 (Only in the Family Enclosure)
Note: Prices vary depending on the category of the game.
Programme Price: £3.00

DISABLED INFORMATION

Wheelchairs: 250 spaces available in areas throughout the ground. A similar number of places are available for the ambulant disabled and visually impaired
Helpers: One helper admitted for each disabled supporter
Prices: Registered disabled supporters are admitted for half the normal prices £16.50 – £33.50. Helpers are admitted free
Disabled Toilets: Many available throughout the ground
Free commentaries are available for the visually impaired
Contact: (020) 7619-5050 (Bookings are necessary)

Travelling Supporters' Information:
As the stadium is situated in a mainly residential area, only car owners with resident's permits will be allowed to park in the designated on-street parking areas. Cars parked illegally will be towed away so use public transport whenever possible. The nearest tube station is Arsenal (Piccadilly Line) which is 3 minutes walk from the ground with Finsbury Park (Victoria & Piccadilly Lines) and Highbury & Islington about 10 minutes walk away.

ASTON VILLA FC

Founded: 1874 (**Entered League**: 1888)
Former Names: None
Nicknames: 'The Villans' 'Villa'
Ground: Villa Park, Trinity Road, Birmingham B6 6HE
Ground Capacity: 42,585 (All seats)
Record Attendance: 76,588 (2nd March 1946)
Pitch Size: 115 × 75 yards

Colours: Claret shirts with Blue sleeves, White shorts with Claret & Blue trim
Telephone Nº: (0121) 327-2299
Fax Number: (0121) 322-2107
Consumer Sales: 0800 612-0970
Consumer Sales Fax Number: 0800 612-0977
Web Site: www.avfc.co.uk

GENERAL INFORMATION

Ground Tours: 0800 612-0970
Car Parking: Aston Villa Events Centre Car Park in Aston Hall Road.
Away Coach Parking: Opposite the ground
Nearest Railway Station: Witton or Aston (5 mins. walk)
Nearest Bus Station: Birmingham Centre
Club Shop: 'Villa Village' at the ground + also at New Street in Birmingham City Centre
Opening Times: Monday to Saturday 9.00am to 5.00pm, Sundays 10.00am to 2.00pm, Sunday Matchdays 4 hours before kick-off and 1 hour after the final whistle.
City Centre shop open 9.30am to 6.00pm Monday to Saturday, 11.00am to 3.00pm on Sundays.
Telephone Nº: 0800 612-0970
Police Telephone Nº: 0845 113-5000

GROUND INFORMATION

Away Supporters' Entrances & Sections:
Doug Ellis Stand – Blocks 'P' & 'Q'

ADMISSION INFO (2009/2010 PRICES)

Adult Seating: £15.00 – £39.00
Child Seating: £10.00 – £39.00
Senior Citizen Seating: £12.00 – £21.00
Note: Prices vary depending on the category of the game
Programme Price: £2.50

DISABLED INFORMATION

Wheelchairs: 84 spaces in total in the Trinity Road Stand lower, 8 of which are for away supporters
Helpers: Admitted on request – one per disabled fan
Prices: £20.00–£25.00 for each disabled supporter & helper
Disabled Toilets: Available in the Trinity Road Stand lower
Contact: 0800 612-0970 ext. 344 (Bookings are necessary)
E-mail contact: disability@avfc.co.uk

Travelling Supporters' Information: From all parts: Exit M6 at Junction 6 (Spaghetti Junction). Follow signs for Birmingham (NE). Take the 4th exit at the roundabout onto the A38 (M) signposted Aston. After ½ mile, turn right into Aston Hall Road.
Bus Services: Service 7 from Colmore Circus to Witton Square. Also some specials.

BARNET FC ✓

Founded: 1888
Former Names: Barnet Alston FC
Nickname: 'The Bees'
Ground: Underhill Stadium, Barnet Lane, Barnet, Herts. EN5 2DN
Record Attendance: 11,026 (1952)
Pitch Size: 110 × 70 yards

Colours: Shirts and shorts are Black with Amber Trim
Telephone Nº: (020) 8441-6932
Ticket Office: (020) 8449-6325
Fax Number: (020) 8447-0655
Ground Capacity: 5,567
Seating Capacity: 2,200 approximately
Web site: www.barnetfc.com

GENERAL INFORMATION

Supporters Club: K. Doe, c/o Club
Telephone Nº: –
Car Parking: Street Parking and High Barnet Underground Car Park
Coach Parking: By Police Direction
Nearest Railway Station: New Barnet (1½ miles)
Nearest Tube Station: High Barnet (Northern) (5 minutes walk)
Club Shop: Located at the South End of the ground
Opening Times: Monday to Friday 9.30am to 5.30pm and Saturday Matchdays from 11.00am to 5.30pm
Telephone Nº: (020) 8441-6932
Police Telephone Nº: (020) 8200-2212

GROUND INFORMATION

Away Supporters' Entrances & Sections:
Entrances in Westcombe Drive for the North East Terrace and seating areas

ADMISSION INFO (2009/2010 PRICES)

Adult Standing: £13.00 – £15.00
Adult Seating: £20.00 (£16.00 in the Family Stand)
Concessionary Seating: £12.00
Under-18/Senior Citizen Standing: £5 – £7 (Members)
Away Supporters: £15.00 Standing; £16.00 Seating
Under-12 Members: Admitted free of charge
Family Tickets: Available in the Family Stand when purchased in advance: £30.00 (2 adults + 2 Under-18s)
Programme Price: £2.50

DISABLED INFORMATION

Wheelchairs: 8 covered spaces in total for Home and Away fans on the North Terrace – Barnet Lane Entrance
Helpers: One helper admitted per wheelchair
Prices: Free of charge
Disabled Toilets: One available in the Social Club
Are Bookings Necessary: 24 hours notice required
Contact: (020) 8441-6932 (Wendy Ayre)

Travelling Supporters' Information:
Routes: The ground is situated off the Great North Road (A1000) at the foot of Barnet Hill near to the junction with Station Road (A110). Barnet Lane is on the west of the A1000 next to the Cricket Ground.

BARNSLEY FC

Founded: 1887 (**Entered League**: 1898)
Former Names: Barnsley St. Peter's
Nickname: 'Reds'
Ground: Oakwell Stadium, Barnsley S71 1ET
Ground Capacity: 23,176 (All seats)
Record Attendance: 40,255 (15th February 1936)
Pitch Size: 110 × 72 yards

Colours: Red shirts with White shorts and Red socks
Telephone Nº: (01226) 211211
Ticket Office: 0871 226-6777
Fax Number: (01226) 211444
Web Site: www.barnsleyfc.co.uk

GENERAL INFORMATION

Car Parking: Queen's Ground Car Park (adjacent)
Coach Parking: Queen's Ground Car Park
Nearest Railway Station: Barnsley Interchange (6 minutes walk)
Nearest Bus Station: Barnsley Interchange
Club Shop: At the Stadium
Opening Times: Monday to Friday 9.00am to 5.00pm. Saturdays 9.00am to 2.00pm. Saturday Matchdays open 9.00am to 3.00pm then 4.45pm to 5.15pm. Evening matchdays open 9.00am to 7.45pm
Telephone Nº: (01226) 211400
Police Telephone Nº: (0114) 220-2020

GROUND INFORMATION

Away Supporters' Entrances & Sections:
North Stand Turnstiles 42-51

ADMISSION INFO (2009/2010 PRICES)

Adult Seating: £19.00 – £21.00
Child Seating: £5.00 – £12.00
Concessionary Seating: £11.00 – £12.00
Programme Price: £3.00

DISABLED INFORMATION

Wheelchairs: A disabled stand provides accommodation to those in wheelchairs and blind supporters.
Helpers: Admitted depending on room available
Prices: £19.00 for the disabled but helpers are admitted free of charge
Disabled Toilets: Available in the Corner Stand, North Stand and C.K. Beckett Stand
Commentaries are available for the blind
Contact: 0871 226-6777 (Bookings are necessary)

Travelling Supporters' Information: From All Parts: Exit the M1 at Junction 37 and follow the 'Barnsley FC/Football Ground' signs which lead to a large surface car park adjacent to the stadium (2 miles).

BIRMINGHAM CITY FC

Founded: 1875 (**Entered League**: 1892)
Former Names: Small Heath Alliance FC (1875-88); Small Heath FC (1888-1905); Birmingham FC (1905-45)
Nickname: 'Blues'
Ground: St. Andrew's Stadium, Birmingham B9 4RL
Ground Capacity: 30,079 (All seats)
Record Attendance: 68,844 (11th February 1939)
Pitch Size: 110 × 73 yards
Colours: Royal Blue and White Shirts, White Shorts and Blue and White socks
Telephone Nº: 0844 557-1875
Ticket Office: 0844 557-1875 Option 2
Fax Number: 0844 557-1975
Web Site: www.bcfc.com

GENERAL INFORMATION

Car Parking: Street Parking + Birmingham Wheels (secure)
Coach Parking: Coventry Road
Nearest Railway Station: Birmingham New Street or Birmingham Moor Street (20 minutes walk)
Nearest Bus Station: Digbeth
Club Shops: St. Andrew's Superstore at the ground
Opening Times: Monday to Saturday 9.30am to 5.30pm
Telephone Nº: 0844 557-1875 Option 4
Police Telephone Nº: 0845 113-5000

GROUND INFORMATION

Away Supporters' Entrances & Sections:
Gil Merrick Stand, Coventry Road

ADMISSION INFO (2009/2010 PRICES)

Adult Seating: £10.00 – £35.00
Child Seating: £5.00 – £19.00
Note: Prices vary depending on the match category
Programme Price: £3.00

DISABLED INFORMATION

Wheelchairs: Spaces available in the Spion Kop Stand, Family Stand, Gil Merrick Lower Stand and Tilton Road Stand
Helpers: One assistant admitted for each disabled fan
Prices: £20.00 for each disabled fan plus an assistant
Disabled Toilets: Available in the Spion Kop Stand, Family Stand, Gil Merrick Stand and Tilton Road Stand
Contact: 0844 557-1875 Option 2 (Bookings are necessary)

Travelling Supporters' Information: From All Parts: Exit M6 at Junction 6 and take the A38 (M) (Aston Expressway). Leave at 2nd exit then take first exit at roundabout along the Dartmouth Middleway. After 1¼ miles turn left on to Coventry Road.
Bus Services: Services 96 & 97 from Birmingham; Services 98 & 99 from Digbeth.

BLACKBURN ROVERS FC

Founded: 1875 (**Entered League**: 1888)
Nickname: 'Rovers' 'Blues & Whites'
Ground: Ewood Park, Blackburn, Lancashire BB2 4JF
Pitch Size: 115 × 72 yards
Ground Capacity: 31,154 (All seats)
Record Attendance: 62,255 vs Bolton (2/3/1929)

Colours: Blue and White halved shirts, White shorts
Telephone Nº: 0871 702-1875
Ticket Office: 0871 222-1444
Fax Number: (01254) 671042
Web Site: www.rovers.co.uk

GENERAL INFORMATION

Car Parking: 800 spaces available at the ground
Coach Parking: At the ground
Nearest Railway Station: Blackburn Central (1½ miles)
Nearest Bus Station: Blackburn Central (1½ miles)
Club Shop: At the ground
Opening Times: Monday to Saturday 9.00am – 5.00pm; Saturday Matchdays 9.00am–3.00pm and 4.45pm–5.30pm; Sundays 12.00pm – 3.00pm
Telephone Nº: (01254) 695348
Police Telephone Nº: (01254) 51212

GROUND INFORMATION

Away Supporters' Entrances & Sections: Darwen End

ADMISSION INFO (2009/2010 PRICES)

Adult Seating: £17.00 – £38.00
Child Seating: £7.00 – £20.00
Concessions Seating: £12.00 – £28.00
Note: Prices vary depending on the category of the game
Programme Price: £3.00

DISABLED INFORMATION

Wheelchairs: 262 spaces in total for Home and Away fans
Helpers: One helper admitted per disabled fan. Please note that applications for helpers tickets must be made in advance
Prices: 70% off usual prices for the disabled. Free for helpers
Disabled Toilets: 14 purpose-built ground level toilets
Commentaries available by arrangement for up to 6 people
Contact: 0871 702-1875 (Bookings are necessary)

Travelling Supporters' Information: Routes: Supporters travelling Northbound on the M6: Exit the M6 at Junction 29, follow the M65 and exit at Junction 4 for Ewood Park. The ground is ¾ mile from Junction 4 – please look for parking areas to avoid congestion around the ground; Supporters travelling Northbound on the M61: Exit the M61 at Junction 9, join the M65 and exit at Junction 4 (then as above); Supporters travelling Southbound on the M6: Exit the M6 at Junction 30, follow the M61 and exit at Junction 9 onto the M65. Exit the M65 at Junction 4 for the ground; Supporters from the Yorkshire Area either on the B6234, the A56 Haslingden by-pass or the A59 Skipton Road – please follow signs for Ewood Park (follow Preston M65 and exit at Junction 4).

BLACKPOOL FC

Founded: 1887 (**Entered League**: 1896)
Former Name: Merged with Blackpool St.Johns (1887)
Nickname: 'Seasiders' or 'Tangerines'
Ground: Bloomfield Road, Blackpool, FY1 6JJ
Ground Capacity: 16,000 (All seats)
Record Attendance: 38,098 (17th September 1955)
Pitch Size: 110 × 74 yards

Colours: Tangerine shirts with White shorts
Telephone N°: 0870 443-1953
Ticket Office: 0870 443-1953
Fax Number: (01253) 405011
Web Site: www.blackpoolfc.co.uk

GENERAL INFORMATION

Car Parking: 3,000 spaces at the ground and street parking
Coach Parking: Available at the ground
Nearest Railway Station: Blackpool South (5 mins. walk)
Nearest Bus Station: Talbot Road (2 miles)
Club Shop: At the ground
Opening Times: Daily from 9.00am to 5.15pm
Telephone N°: 0870 443-1953

GROUND INFORMATION

Away Supporters' Entrances & Sections:
East Stand (Uncovered)

ADMISSION INFO (2009/2010 PRICES)

Adult Seating: £20.00 – £24.50
Under-19s Seating: £11.00 – £16.50
Under-16s Seating: £10.00 – £14.50
Under-12s Seating: £6.00 – £12.00
Senior Citizen Seating: £15.00 – £19.50
Programme Price: £2.50

DISABLED INFORMATION

Wheelchairs: Over 50 spaces in total for home and away fans in the new North and West Stands
Helpers: One helper admitted per disabled fan
Prices: £12.00 for the Disabled
Disabled Toilets: Available
Contact: 0870 443-1953 (Bookings are necessary)

Travelling Supporters' Information: From All Parts: Exit M6 at Junction 32 onto the M55. Follow signs for the main car parks along the new 'spine' road to the car parks at the side of the ground.

BOLTON WANDERERS FC

Founded: 1874 (**Entered League:** 1888)
Former Names: Christchurch FC (1874-1877)
Nickname: 'Trotters'
Ground: Reebok Stadium, Burnden Way, Lostock, Bolton, Lancashire BL6 6JW
Ground Capacity: 27,879 (All seats)
Pitch Size: 110 × 70 yards

Record Attendance: 27,409
Colours: White shirts and shorts
Telephone Nº: (01204) 673673
Ticket Office: 0871 871-2932
Fax Number: 0871 871-8183
Web Site: www.bwfc.co.uk

GENERAL INFORMATION

Car Parking: 2,800 spaces available at the ground
Coach Parking: Available at the ground
Nearest Railway Station: Horwich Parkway (600 yards)
Nearest Bus Station: Moor Lane, Bolton
Club Shop: At the ground
Opening Times: Daily from 9.30am to 5.30pm
Telephone Nº: (01204) 673650
Police Telephone Nº: (01204) 522466

GROUND INFORMATION

Away Supporters' Entrances & Sections:
South Stand entrances and accommodation

ADMISSION INFO (2009/2010 PRICES)

Adult Seating: £20.00 – £38.00
Child Seating: £9.00 – £20.00
Senior Citizen Seating: £15.00 – £27.00
Note: Prices vary depending on the category of the game and special family tickets are also available
Programme Price: £2.50

DISABLED INFORMATION

Wheelchairs: 32 spaces available for visiting fans, 72 spaces for home fans
Helpers: One helper admitted per disabled fan
Prices: Free for wheelchair users. Helpers normal prices
Disabled Toilets: Yes
Contact: (01204) 673673 (Bookings are necessary)

Travelling Supporters' Information:
From All Parts: Exit the M61 at Junction 6 and the ground is clearly visible ¼ mile away.

AFC BOURNEMOUTH

Founded: 1899 (Entered League: 1923)
Former Names: Boscombe FC (1899-1923); Bournemouth & Boscombe Athletic FC (1923-1972)
Nickname: 'Cherries'
Ground: Dean Court, Bournemouth, Dorset BH7 7AF
Ground Capacity: 9,776 (All seats)
Record Attendance: 9,632 (6th November 2007)
Pitch Size: 115 × 74 yards
Colours: Red & Black shirts with Black shorts
Telephone Nº: (01202) 726300
Ticket Office: (01202) 726338
Fax Number: (01202) 726373
Web Site: www.afcb.co.uk

GENERAL INFORMATION

Car Parking: Car Park for 600 cars behind Main Stand
Coach Parking: At the ground
Nearest Railway Station: Bournemouth Central (1½ miles)
Nearest Bus Stop: Holdenhurst Road, Bournemouth
Club Shop: At the ground
Opening Times: Monday to Friday 9.00am to 5.00pm and Saturday Matchdays from 9.00am to kick-off
Telephone Nº: (01202) 726325
Police Telephone Nº: (01202) 552099

GROUND INFORMATION

Away Supporters' Entrances & Sections:
East Stand turnstiles 'F' 14-16 for East Stand accommodation (Away ticket office is adjacent)

ADMISSION INFO (2009/2010 PRICES)

Adult Seating: £14.00 – £28.00
Child Seating: £7.00 – £17.00
Concessionary Seating: £7.00 – £17.00
Note: Family tickets are also available
Programme Price: £3.00

DISABLED INFORMATION

Wheelchairs: Spaces available in all stands
Helpers: One helper admitted per disabled fan
Prices: Free of charge for both the disabled and helpers
Disabled Toilets: Available in all Stands
Contact: (07803) 090047 (Bookings are necessary)

Travelling Supporters' Information: Routes: From the North & East: Take the A338 into Bournemouth and turn left at 'Kings Park' turning. After the slip road go straight forward at the mini-roundabout into Kings Park Drive – a car park is 500 yards on the left and the ground is nearby; From the West: Use the A3049, turning right at Wallisdown Roundabout to Talbot Roundabout. Take the first exit at Talbot Roundabout (over Wessex Way), then left at the mini-roundabout. Go straight on at the traffic lights then right at the mini-roundabout into Kings Park for the ground.

BRADFORD CITY FC

Founded: 1903 (**Entered League**: 1903)
Nickname: 'Bantams'
Ground: Coral Windows Stadium, Valley Parade, Bradford BD8 7DY
Ground Capacity: 25,134 (All seats)
Record Attendance: 39,146 (11th March 1911)
Pitch Size: 113 × 70 yards
Colours: Claret and Amber shirts with Claret shorts
Telephone Nº: (01274) 773355
Ticket Office: (01274) 770012
Fax Number: (01274) 773356
Marketing Department: (01274) 706840
Web Site: www.bradfordcityfc.co.uk

GENERAL INFORMATION

Car Parking: Street Parking and Car Parks (£3.00 charge)
Coach Parking: By Police direction
Nearest Railway Station: Bradford Foster Square
Nearest Bus Station: Bradford Interchange (1 mile)
Club Shop: At the ground
Opening Times: Monday to Friday 9.00am to 5.00pm, Saturday 9.00am to 3.00pm
Telephone Nº: (01274) 706847
Police Telephone Nº: (01274) 723422

GROUND INFORMATION

Away Supporters' Entrances & Sections:
Midland Road Stand entrances and accommodation

ADMISSION INFO (2009/2010 PRICES)

Adult Seating: £20.00
Child Seating: £12.00
Note: Special concessions are available in the Family Stand
Programme Price: £2.50

DISABLED INFORMATION

Wheelchairs: 100 spaces available in total for Home and Away fans in the disabled area, 'A' Block of Sunwin Stand and also in the Carlsberg Stand & East Stand
Helpers: One helper admitted per disabled fan
Prices: Half-price for disabled fans and helpers
Disabled Toilets: Available behind the disabled area
Contact: (01274) 770012 (Bookings are necessary)

Travelling Supporters' Information: Routes: Exit the M62 at Junction 26 and take the M606 towards Bradford. At the end of the motorway get in the middle lane and follow signs for Bradford (West) into Rooley Lane (signs for the Airport). A McDonalds is now on your left. Turn left into Wakefield Road at the roundabout and stay in the middle lane. Continue straight on over two roundabouts (signs to Shipley and Skipton) onto Shipley Airedale Road which then becomes Canal Road. Just after Tesco on the left, turn left into Station Road and left again into Queens Road. Go up the hill to the third set of traffic lights and turn left into Manningham Lane. After the Gulf petrol station on the left, turn first left into Valley Parade for the Stadium.

BRENTFORD FC

Founded: 1889 (**Entered League:** 1920)
Nickname: 'The Bees'
Ground: Griffin Park, Braemar Road, Brentford, Middlesex TW8 0NT
Ground Capacity: 12,800
Seating Capacity: 10,200
Record Attendance: 39,626 (5th March 1938)

Pitch Size: 110 × 74 yards
Colours: Red & White striped shirts with Black shorts
Telephone Nº: 0845 3456-442
Ticket Office: 0845 3456-442
Fax Number: (020) 8568-9940
Web Site: www.brentfordfc.co.uk

GENERAL INFORMATION

Car Parking: Street Parking
Coach Parking: By Police direction
Nearest Railway Station: Brentford (½ mile)
Nearest Tube Station: South Ealing (Piccadilly) (1 mile)
Club Shop: At the ground in Braemar Road
Opening Times: Weekdays 10.00am–4.00pm and Matchdays 12.00pm – 6.00pm
Telephone Nº: 0845 3456-442
Police Telephone Nº: (020) 8569-9728

GROUND INFORMATION

Away Supporters' Entrances & Sections:
Brook Road Upper and Lower for both seating and terracing

ADMISSION INFO (2009/2010 PRICES)

Adult Standing: £20.00
Adult Seating: £21.00 or £22.00
Juniors Standing/Seating: £5.00
Students/Senior Citizen Standing: £12.00 or £14.00
Students/Senior Citizen Seating: £15.00 or £16.00
Programme Price: £3.00

DISABLED INFORMATION

Wheelchairs: 10 spaces for Home fans, 2 spaces for Away fans in the disabled section, Braemar Road
Helpers: One helper admitted per disabled fan
Prices: Normal prices for the disabled. Free for helpers
Disabled Toilets: Available in the disabled section
Commentaries are available for the blind
Contact: 0845 3456-442 (Bookings are necessary)

Travelling Supporters' Information: Routes: From the North: Take the A406 North Circular (from the M1/A1) to the Chiswick Roundabout and then along the Great West Road and turn left at the third set of traffic lights into Ealing Road for the ground; From the East: Take the A406 to the Chiswick Roundabout, then as North; From the West: Exit M4 at Junction 2 – down to the Chiswick Roundabout, then as North; From the South: Use the A3, M3, A240 or A316 to Kew Road, continue along over Kew Bridge, turn left at the traffic lights, then right at the next traffic lights into Ealing Road.

✓ OLD

BRIGHTON & HOVE ALBION FC

Founded: 1901 (**Entered League**: 1920)
Nickname: 'Seagulls'
Office: North West Suite, 8th Floor, Tower Point, 44 North Road, Brighton BN1 1YR
Ground: Withdean Stadium, Tongdean Lane, off London Road, Brighton BN1 5JD
Ground Capacity: 8,676 (All seats)
Pitch Size: 110 × 70 yards
Record Attendance: 8,691 (at Withdean Stadium)
Colours: Blue & White striped shirts, White shorts
Telephone Nº: (01273) 695400
Ticket Office: (01273) 776992
Ticket Office Address: 5 Queen's Road, Brighton
Fax Number: (01273) 648179
Web Site: www.seagulls.co.uk

GENERAL INFORMATION

Car Parking: No parking near the stadium – take park & ride buses or walk
Coach Parking: By Police direction
Nearest Railway Station: Preston Park (10 minutes walk)
Nearest Bus Station: Brighton
Club Shop: 5/6 Queen's Road, Brighton
Opening Times: Monday–Saturday 9.30am-5.30pm (shop closes at 5.00pm on Home matchdays)
Telephone Nº: (01273) 776969

GROUND INFORMATION

Away Supporters' Entrances & Sections:
West Stand (Block X)

ADMISSION INFO (2009/2010 PRICES)

Adult Seating: £23.50 – £27.00
Child Seating: £14.00 – £17.00
Senior Citizen Seating: £15.50 – £18.50
Note: Advanced booking only – no tickets are available at the ground (matches are always all-ticket).
Programme Price: £3.00

DISABLED INFORMATION

Wheelchairs: Limited spaces for Home fans in the disabled section, South Stand and Away fans in the West Stand
Helpers: One helper admitted per disabled person
Prices: £16.50 for the disabled. Helpers are admitted free
Disabled Toilets: Yes
Contact: (01273) 776992 (Bookings are necessary)

Travelling Supporters' Information: Routes: From the North: Take the M23 then the A23 to Brighton. The ground is situated in Tongdean Lane which is directly off the A23 (London Road) just after Peacock Lane but, as no parking is available around the ground, a park and ride scheme will operate from Mill Road which is close to the junction of the A23 and the A27; From the East and West: Take the A27 into Brighton to the A23 then as above.

BRISTOL CITY FC

Founded: 1894 (Entered League: 1901)
Former Name: Bristol South End FC (1894-1897)
Nickname: 'The Robins'
Ground: Ashton Gate Stadium, Bristol BS3 2EJ
Ground Capacity: 21,497 (All seats)
Pitch Size: 115 × 75 yards
Record Attendance: 43,335 (16th February 1935)

Colours: Red shirts with White shorts
Telephone Nº: 0871 222-6666
Ticket Hotline: 0871 222-6666
Fax Number: (0117) 963-0700
Web Site: www.bcfc.co.uk

GENERAL INFORMATION

Car Parking: Street parking
Coach Parking: Ashton Vale Trading Estate (contact Police)
Nearest Railway Station: Bristol Temple Meads (1½ miles)
Nearest Bus Station: Bristol City Centre
Club Shop: At the ground
Opening Times: Monday 10.00am to 5.00pm, Tuesday to Friday 9.00am to 5.00pm and Saturdays 9.00am to 12.00pm (open until kick-off on Matchdays)
Telephone Nº: 0871 222-6666
Police Telephone Nº: (0117) 927-7777

GROUND INFORMATION

Away Supporters' Entrances & Sections:
Wedlock Stand

ADMISSION INFO (2009/2010 PRICES)

Adult Seating: £25.00 – £30.00
Under-16s Seating: £15.00 – £21.00
Concessionary Seating: £20.00 – £24.00
Note: A membership scheme is available which offers discounted prices for advance bookings
Programme Price: £3.00

DISABLED INFORMATION

Wheelchairs: Limited number accommodated at pitchside – please apply early
Helpers: One helper admitted per disabled fan
Prices: Normal prices for the disabled. Free for helpers
Disabled Toilets: 2 available
Commentaries are available for the blind (contact the club for further information)
Contact: 0871 222-6666 (Bookings are necessary)

Travelling Supporters' Information: Routes: From the North & West: Exit the M5 at Junction 16, take the A38 to Bristol City Centre and follow the A38 Taunton signs. Cross the swing bridge after 1¼ miles and bear left into Winterstoke Road for the ground; From the East: Take the M4 then M32 and follow signs for the City Centre. Then as for North and West; From the South: Exit the M5 at Junction 18 and follow Taunton signs over the swing bridge (then as above).
Bus Services: Services 27A and 28A from the Railway Station.

BRISTOL ROVERS FC

Founded: 1883 (**Entered League**: 1920)
Former Names: Black Arabs FC (1883-84); Eastville Rovers FC (1884-96); Bristol Eastville Rovers FC (1896-97)
Nickname: 'Pirates' 'Rovers' 'Gas'
Ground: Memorial Stadium, Filton Avenue, Horfield, Bristol BS7 0BF
Pitch Size: 110 × 71 yards

Ground Capacity: 11,917
Seating Capacity: 3,307
Record Attendance: 12,011 (9th March 2008)
Colours: Blue & White quartered shirts, White shorts
Telephone Nº: (0117) 909-6648
Fax Number: (0117) 908-5530
Web Site: www.bristolrovers.co.uk

GENERAL INFORMATION

Car Parking: Very limited number of spaces at the ground and street parking
Coach Parking: At the ground
Nearest Railway Station: Temple Meads (2 miles)
Nearest Bus Station: Bristol City Centre
Club Shop: 199 Two Mile Hill Road, Kingswood and also at Pirate Leisure, Memorial Stadium, Filton Avenue
Opening Times: Supporters' Club: Weekdays 9.00am to 5.00pm and Saturdays 9.00am to 1.00pm; Pirate Leisure: Weekdays 9.00am to 5.00pm, Saturdays 9.00am to 1.00pm (Home matchdays 9.00am – 3.00pm then 4.45pm – 5.15pm)
Telephone Nº: (0117) 961-1772 + (0117) 909-6648

GROUND INFORMATION

Away Supporters' Entrances & Sections:
Entrance to Uplands Terrace & South Stand via Filton Avenue

ADMISSION INFO (2009/2010 PRICES)

Adult Standing: £17.00–£19.00
Adult Seating: £20.00 – £25.00
Child Standing: £5.00 – £11.00
Child Seating: £10.00 – £19.50
Discounts are available if tickets are bought before matchdays
Programme Price: £3.00

DISABLED INFORMATION

Wheelchairs: Unspecified number accommodated in front of the Uplands Stand and DAS Stand
Helpers: One helper admitted per disabled person
Prices: £10.00 for wheelchair and ambulant disabled. Helpers are admitted free of charge
Disabled Toilets: In the Uplands Stand and DAS Stand
Contact: (0117) 909-6648 (Bookings are necessary)

Travelling Supporters' Information: Routes: From All Parts: Exit the M32 at Junction 2 then take the exit at the roundabout (signposted Horfield) into Muller Road. Continue for approximately 1½ miles passing straight across 3 sets of traffic lights. At the 6th set of traffic lights turn left into Filton Avenue and the ground is immediately on the left.

BURNLEY FC

Founded: 1882 (**Entered League**: 1888)
Former Name: Burnley Rovers FC
Nickname: 'Clarets'
Ground: Turf Moor, Harry Potts Way, Burnley, Lancashire BB10 4BX
Ground Capacity: 22,700 (All seats)
Record Attendance: 54,775 (23rd February 1924)

Pitch Size: 112 × 70 yards
Colours: Claret and Blue shirts with White shorts
Telephone Nº: 0871 221-1882
Ticket Office: 0871 221-1914
Fax Number: (01282) 700014
Web Site: www.burnleyfc.com

GENERAL INFORMATION

Car Parking: Ormerod Road, adjacent to the Fire Station (2 minutes walk)
Coach Parking: By Police direction
Nearest Railway Station: Burnley Central (1½ miles)
Nearest Bus Station: Burnley (5 minutes walk)
Club Shop: At the ground
Opening Times: Monday to Friday 9.00am – 6.00pm; Saturdays 9.00am – 5.00pm
Telephone Nº: 0871 221-1882
Police Telephone Nº: (01282) 425001

GROUND INFORMATION

Away Supporters' Entrances & Sections:
David Fishwick Stand

ADMISSION INFO (2009/2010 PRICES)

Adult Seating: £26.00 – £35.00
Under-16s Seating: £13.00 – £19.00
Programme Price: £3.00

DISABLED INFORMATION

Wheelchairs: Three designated wheelchair areas
Helpers: One helper admitted for each wheelchair user
Prices: £35.00 for each disabled fan plus one helper admitted free of charge
Disabled Toilets: Available
Commentaries are available via headsets
Non-wheelchair disabled, please phone for further details
Contact: 0871 221-1914 (Bookings are necessary)

Travelling Supporters' Information: Routes: From the North: Follow the A682 to the Town Centre and take first exit at roundabout (Gala Club) into Yorkshire Street. Follow through traffic signals into Harry Potts Way; From the East: Follow the A646 to the A671 then along Todmorden Road towards the Town Centre. At the traffic signals (crossroads) turn right into Harry Potts Way; From the West & South: Exit the M6 at Junction 29 onto the M65. Exit the M65 at Junction 10 and follow signs for Burnley Football Club. At the roundabout in the town centre take the third exit into Yorkshire Street. Then as from the North.

BURTON ALBION FC

Founded: 1950 (**Entered League**: 2009)
Former Names: None
Nickname: 'The Brewers'
Ground: The Pirelli Stadium, Princess Way, Burton-on-Trent DE13 0AR
Record Attendance: 6,192 (17th April 2009)
Pitch Size: 110 × 72 yards

Colours: Shirts are Yellow with Black trim, shorts are Black with Yellow Trim
Telephone Nº: (01283) 565938
Fax Number: (01283) 523199
Ground Capacity: 6,200
Seating Capacity: 2,000
Web site: www.burtonalbionfc.co.uk

GENERAL INFORMATION

Supporters Club: c/o Club
Telephone Nº: (01283) 565938
Car Parking: Available at the ground
Coach Parking: Rykneld Trading Estate, Derby Road
Nearest Railway Station: Burton-on-Trent (1½ miles)
Nearest Bus Station: Burton-on-Trent (1½ miles)
Club Shop: At the ground
Opening Times: Weekdays 8.30am – 5.30pm and Matchdays from 1½ hours before kick-off
Telephone Nº: (01283) 565938
Police Telephone Nº: 0854 330-2010

GROUND INFORMATION

Away Supporters' Entrances & Sections:
East Stand, Derby Road

ADMISSION INFO (2009/2010 PRICES)

Adult Standing: £13.00
Adult Seating: £15.00
Child Standing: £4.00
Child Seating: £6.00
Senior Citizen Standing: £11.00
Senior Citizen Seating: £13.00
Programme Price: £3.00

DISABLED INFORMATION

Wheelchairs: Over 78 spaces available for home and away fans in the designated disabled areas
Helpers: Admitted
Prices: Normal prices for the disabled. Free for helpers
Disabled Toilets: Available in all stands
Contact: (01283) 565938 (Bookings are necessary)

Travelling Supporters' Information:
Routes: From the M1, North and South: Exit at Junction 23A and join the A50 towards Derby (also signposted for Alton Towers). Join the A38 southbound at the Toyota factory (towards Burton & Lichfield) then exit for Burton North onto the A5121. Continue past the Pirelli factory on the right and the BP Garage and Cash & Carry on the left then turn into Princess Way at the roundabout; From the M5/6 South: Join the M42 northbound and exit onto the A446 signposted Lichfield. Follow signs for the A38 to Burton then exit onto A5121 as above; From the M6 North: Exit at Junction 15 and follow the A50 towards Stoke and Uttoxeter. Exit the A50 for the A38 southbound signposted Burton and Lichfield at the Toyota factory, then as above.

BURY FC

Founded: 1885 (**Entered League**: 1894)
Nickname: 'Shakers'
Ground: Gigg Lane, Bury, Lancashire BL9 9HR
Ground Capacity: 11,669 (All seats)
Pitch Size: 112 × 70 yards
Record Attendance: 35,000 (9th January 1960)

Colours: Chocolate and Sky Blue shirts, White shorts
Telephone Nº: (0161) 764-4881
Ticket Office: (0161) 764-4881
General Fax Number: (0161) 764-5521
Commercial Dept. Fax Number: (0161) 763-3103
Web Site: www.buryfc.co.uk

GENERAL INFORMATION

Car Parking: Designated car parks only
Coach Parking: By Police direction
Nearest Railway Station: Bury Interchange (1 mile)
Nearest Bus Station: Bury Interchange
Club Shop: At the ground
Opening Times: Monday to Friday and Saturday matchdays 9.00am to 5.00pm
Telephone Nº: (0161) 762-0528
Police Telephone Nº: (0161) 872-5050

GROUND INFORMATION

Away Supporters' Entrances & Sections:
Gigg Lane entrance for the West Stand

ADMISSION INFO (2009/2010 PRICES)

Adult Seating: £15.00 – £17.00
Child/Senior Citizen Seating: £10.00 (Over-64s qualify)
Young Persons Seating (Ages 16-21): £12.00
Note: Family concessions are also available
Programme Price: £2.50

DISABLED INFORMATION

Wheelchairs: Spaces for 46 wheelchairs in disabled sections (home area) and a further 8 spaces in the Away Supporters' Section
Helpers: One helper admitted per wheelchair
Prices: £10.00 for the disabled. Free of charge for helpers
Disabled Toilets: Available in disabled section
A Radio Commentary is available in the Press Box for the Registered Blind
Contact: (0161) 764-4881 (Bookings are not necessary)

Travelling Supporters' Information: Routes: From the North: Exit the M66 at Junction 2, take Bury Road (A58) for ½ mile, then turn left into Heywood Street and follow this into Parkhills Road until its end, turn left into Manchester Road (A56) and then left again into Gigg Lane. From the South, East and West: Exit the M60 at Junction 17, take Bury Road (A56) for 3 miles and then turn right into Gigg Lane.

CARDIFF CITY FC | ✓ OK

Founded: 1899 (**Entered League**: 1920)
Former Names: Riverside FC (1899-1910)
Nickname: 'Bluebirds'
Ground: Cardiff City Stadium, Cardiff CF11 8SX
Record Attendance: 62,634 (Ninian Park 17/10/59)
Ground Capacity: 26,828 (All seats)
Pitch Size: 110 × 75 yards

Colours: Royal Blue shirts with White shorts
Telephone Nº: 0845 345-1400
Away Support Ticket Office: 0845 345-1405
Fax Number: (029) 2034-1148
Web Site: www.cardiffcityfc.co.uk

GENERAL INFORMATION

Car Parking: Stadium car park and Street Parking
Coach Parking: Stadium car park (adjacent)
Nearest Railway Station: Cardiff Central (1 mile)
Nearest Bus Station: Cardiff Central
Club Shop: At the ground
Opening Times: Weekdays from 9.00am to 5.00pm and Matchdays 10.00am to 3.00pm
Telephone Nº: 0845 345-1485
Postal Sales: Yes (Internet Sales also accepted)
Police Telephone Nº: (029) 2022-2111

GROUND INFORMATION

Away Supporters' Entrances & Sections:
Grange End, Gate 07 – sections 119 to 122

ADMISSION INFO (2009/2010 PRICES)

Adult Seating: £20.00 – £32.00
Concessionary Seating: £10.00 – £24.00
Child Seating: £5.00 – £24.00
Note: Tickets are cheaper if purchased before the matchday
Programme Price: £3.00

DISABLED INFORMATION

Wheelchairs: Numerous spaces available for disabled supporters in all areas of the ground
Helpers: One helper admitted per disabled fan
Prices: Normal prices for the disabled. Helpers admitted free of charge
Disabled Toilets: Available
Contact: 0845 345-1405 (Away fans tickets are normally sold in advance but may be available on the day)

Travelling Supporters' Information:
Routes: From All Parts: Exit M4 at Junction 33 and follow Penarth (A4232) signs. After 6 miles, take the B4267 to Cardiff City Stadium.

CARLISLE UNITED FC

Founded: 1903 (**Entered League**: 1928)
Former Names: Formed with the amalgamation of Shaddongate United FC and Carlisle Red Rose FC
Nickname: 'Cumbrians' 'Blues'
Ground: Brunton Park Stadium, Warwick Road, Carlisle CA1 1LL
Ground Capacity: 16,938
Seating Capacity: 7,737
Record Attendance: 27,500 (5th January 1957)
Pitch Size: 112 × 74 yards
Colours: Royal Blue and White shirts and shorts
Telephone Nº: (01228) 526237
Ticket Office: 0844 371-1921
Fax Number: (01228) 554141
Web Site: www.carlisleunited.co.uk

GENERAL INFORMATION

Car Parking: Rear of Ground via St. Aidans Road
Coach Parking: St. Aidans Road Car Park
Nearest Railway Station: Carlisle Citadel (1 mile)
Nearest Bus Station: Lowther Street, Carlisle
Club Shop: At the ground and in the City Centre
Opening Times: Monday to Saturday 10.00am – 5.30pm
Telephone Nº: (01228) 554138
Police Telephone Nº: (01228) 528191

GROUND INFORMATION

Away Supporters' Entrances & Sections:
Turnstiles 14-16 for the Petteril End or CBS Stand Section 2

ADMISSION INFO (2009/2010 PRICES)

Adult Standing: £16.00
Adult Seating: £20.00
Ages 11-17 Standing: £9.00
Ages 11-17 Seating: £10.00
Under-11s Standing: £3.00 **Under-11s Seating**: £4.00
Senior Citizen Standing: £12.00
Senior Citizen Seating: £14.00
Note: Adult tickets are cheaper prior to the matchday
Programme Price: £2.50

DISABLED INFORMATION

Wheelchairs: 17 spaces for wheelchairs in the disabled section, in front of the New East Stand
Helpers: One helper admitted per disabled fan
Prices: Wheelchair disabled admitted for £2.00. Helpers are admitted free of charge
Disabled Toilets: Yes
Contact: (01228) 526237 (Bookings are recommended)

Travelling Supporters' Information:
Routes: From the North, South and East: Exit the M6 at Junction 43 and follow signs for Carlisle (A69) into Warwick Road for the ground; From the West: Take the A69 straight into Warwick Road.

CHARLTON ATHLETIC FC

Founded: 1905 (**Entered League**: 1921)
Nickname: 'Addicks'
Ground: The Valley, Floyd Road, Charlton, London, SE7 8BL
Ground Capacity: 27,111 (All seats)
Record Attendance: 75,031 (12th February 1938)
Pitch Size: 111 × 73 yards

Colours: Red shirts with White shorts
Telephone Nº: (020) 8333-4000
Ticket Office: 0871 226-1905
Fax Number: (020) 8333-4001
Web Site: www.cafc.co.uk

GENERAL INFORMATION

Car Parking: Street Parking
Coach Parking: By Police direction
Nearest Railway Station: Charlton (2 minutes walk)
Nearest Bus Station: At Charlton Railway Station as above
Club Shop: At the ground
Opening Times: Weekdays 10.00am – 6.00pm
Non-Match Saturdays 10.00am – 2.00pm
Telephone Nº: (020) 8858-0391
Police Telephone Nº: (020) 8853-8212

GROUND INFORMATION

Away Supporters' Entrances & Sections:
Valley Grove/Jimmy Seed Stand

ADMISSION INFO (2008/2009 PRICES)

Adult Seating: £20.00 – £35.00
Child Seating: £5.00 – £25.00
Concessions Seating: £10.00 – £25.00
Programme Price: £3.00

DISABLED INFORMATION

Wheelchairs: 96 spaces available for Home fans in the West and East Stands. 7 spaces available for Away fans in the South (Jimmy Seed) Stand
Helpers: One helper admitted per disabled fan
Prices: Helpers are admitted free of charge. Wheelchair disabled pay concessionary prices
Disabled Toilets: Available in West and East Stands
Commentaries are available – please ring for details
Contact: 0871 226-1905 (Bookings are necessary)

Travelling Supporters' Information:
Routes: From All Parts: Exit the M25 at Junction 2 (A2 London-bound) and follow until the road becomes the A102(M). Take the exit marked Woolwich Ferry and turn right along the A206 Woolwich Road. After approximately 1 mile do a U-turn at the roundabout back along Woolwich Road. At the traffic lights turn left into Charlton Church Lane and Floyd Road is the 2nd left.

CHELSEA FC

Founded: 1905 (**Entered League**: 1905)
Nickname: 'Blues'
Ground: Stamford Bridge, Fulham Road, London, SW6 1HS
Ground Capacity: 41,841 (All seats)
Record Attendance: 82,905 (12th October 1935)
Pitch Size: 113 × 74 yards

Colours: Blue shirts and shorts
Telephone Nº: 0871 984-1955 (UK callers); +44 20-7386-9373 (International callers)
Fax Number: (020) 7381-4831
Web Site: www.chelseafc.com

GENERAL INFORMATION

Car Parking: Pre-booked underground car park at ground
Coach Parking: By Police direction
Nearest Tube Station: Fulham Broadway (District)
Club Shop: Chelsea Megastore – at the ground
Opening Times: Monday to Saturday 10.00am – 6.00pm; Sundays 11.00am–5.00pm; Bank Holidays 11.00am – 5.00pm
Stadium tours are also available
Megastore Telephone Nº: (020) 7565-1490
Police Telephone Nº: (020) 7385-1212

GROUND INFORMATION

Away Supporters' Entrances & Sections:
Shed End

ADMISSION INFO (2009/2010 PRICES)

Adult Seating: £34.00 – £65.00
Child Seating: £14.50 – £22.50
Senior Citizen Seating: £14.50 – £22.00
Note: Discounted prices are available to members and also in the Family Stand and East Upper Stand
Programme Price: £3.00

DISABLED INFORMATION

Disabled Seating: 290 spaces (including helpers) in total for Home and Away fans in the disabled area
Helpers: One helper admitted per disabled person
Prices: Free of charge for the disabled
Disabled Toilets: Available in the East Stand Concourse, West Stand and also in the Matthew Harding Stand
Free commentaries for blind supporters are available
Contact: (020) 7915-1950 (Bookings are necessary)

Travelling Supporters' Information:
Routes: From the North & East: Follow Central London signs from the A1/M1 to Hyde Park Corner, then signs for Guildford (A3) to Knightsbridge (A4). After 1 mile turn left into Fulham Road; From the South: Take the A13 or A24 then the A219 to cross Putney Bridge and follow signs for 'West End' (A304) to join the A308 into Fulham Road; From the West: Take the M4 then A4 to Central London, then follow signs to Westminster (A3220). After ¾ mile, turn right at crossroads into Fulham Road.

CHELTENHAM TOWN FC

Founded: 1892 (Entered League: 1999)
Nickname: 'Robins'
Ground: Whaddon Road, Cheltenham, Gloucestershire GL52 5NA
Ground Capacity: 7,136
Seating Capacity: 4,054
Record Attendance: 8,326 (1956)

Pitch Size: 110 × 72 yards
Colours: Red and White shirts with White shorts
Telephone Nº: (01242) 573558
Fax Number: (01242) 224675
Web Site: www.ctfc.com

GENERAL INFORMATION

Car Parking: No parking is available at the ground. A complementary Park & Ride scheme runs from Cheltenham Race Course
Coach Parking: Please phone for details
Nearest Railway Station: Cheltenham Spa (2½ miles)
Nearest Bus Station: Cheltenham Royal Well
Club Shop: At the ground
Opening Times: Weekdays & Matchdays 10.00am–2.45pm.
Telephone Nº: (01242) 573558
Police Telephone Nº: (01242) 528282

GROUND INFORMATION

Away Supporters' Entrances & Sections:
Carlsberg Stand (entrance from Whaddon Road) or the In2Print Stand

ADMISSION INFO (2009/2010 PRICES)

Adult Standing: £15.00
Adult Seating: £19.00 or £20.00
Child Standing: £5.00 (Under-16s)
Child Seating: £7.00 (Under-16s)
Concessionary Standing: £11.00
Concessionary Seating: £13.00 or £14.00
Programme Price: £3.00

DISABLED INFORMATION

Wheelchairs: Accommodated in front of the Stagecoach West Stand (use main entrance) and in the In 2 Print Stand
Helpers: Admitted free of charge
Prices: Concessionary prices are charged
Disabled Toilets: Available in the In 2 Print Stand, adjacent to the Stagecoach West Stand and in the Social Club
Contact: (01242) 573558 (Bookings are necessary)

Travelling Supporters' Information:
Routes: The ground is situated to the North-East of Cheltenham, 1 mile from the Town Centre off the B4632 (Prestbury Road) – Whaddon Road is to the East of the B4632 just North of Pittville Circus. Road signs in the vicinity indicate 'Whaddon Road/ Cheltenham Town FC'.

CHESTERFIELD FC

Founded: 1866 (**Entered League:** 1899)
Former Names: Chesterfield Municipal FC, Chesterfield Town FC
Nickname: 'Spireites' 'Blues'
Ground: Recreation Ground, Saltergate, Chesterfield S40 4SX
Ground Capacity: 8,502
Seating Capacity: 3,866

Record Attendance: 30,968 (7th April 1939)
Pitch Size: 111 × 71 yards
Colours: Blue shirts with White shorts
Telephone Nº: (01246) 209765
Ticket Office: (01246) 209765
Fax Number: (01246) 556799
Web Site: www.chesterfield-fc.co.uk

GENERAL INFORMATION

Car Parking: Saltergate Car Parks (½ mile)
Coach Parking: By Police direction
Nearest Railway Station: Chesterfield (1 mile)
Nearest Bus Station: Chesterfield
Club Shop: At the ground
Opening Times: Monday to Friday 9.00am to 5.00pm. Saturday 9.00am to 3.00pm on matchdays only
Telephone Nº: (01246) 209765
Police Telephone Nº: (01246) 220100

GROUND INFORMATION

Away Supporters' Entrances & Sections:
Cross Street turnstiles for Cross Street End (open) and Cross Street Inner Wing Stand (seated)

ADMISSION INFO (2009/2010 PRICES)

Adult Standing: £17.00
Adult Seating: £18.00 – £20.00
Child Standing: £7.00
Senior Citizen/Child Seating: £13.00 – £15.00 (£5.00 in the Family Stand or £8.00 in the Compton Street Stand)
Senior Citizen Standing: £10.00
Programme Price: £2.50

DISABLED INFORMATION

Wheelchairs: Approximately 15 spaces each for Home fans under the Saltergate Wing Stand and for Away fans under the Cross Street Inner Wing Stand
Helpers: One helper admitted per disabled person
Prices: Concessionary prices for the disabled. One helper admitted free of charge with each disabled fan.
Disabled Toilets: One available underneath the Main Stand
Contact: (01246) 209765 (Bookings are necessary)

Travelling Supporters' Information:
Routes: From the North: Exit the M1 at Junction 30 then take the A619 into the Town Centre. Follow signs for Old Brampton into Saltergate; From the South and East: Take the A617 into the Town Centre (then as from the North); From the West: Take the A619 and when into the Town take the 1st exit at the roundabout into Foljambe Road. Follow to the end of the road, then turn right into Saltergate.

√ old

COLCHESTER UNITED FC

Founded: 1937 (**Entered League:** 1950)
Former Names: The Eagles FC & Colchester Town FC
Nickname: 'U's'
Ground: Weston Homes Community Stadium, United Way, Colchester CO4 5UP
Ground Capacity: 10,000 (All seats)
Record Attendance: 19,072 (27/11/48 – Layer Road)
Pitch Size: 112 × 72 yards

Colours: Royal blue & white striped shirts with Royal blue shorts and white socks
Telephone Nº: (01206) 755100
Ticket Office: 0845 437-9089
Fax Number: (01206) 755114
Web Site: www.cu-fc.com

GENERAL INFORMATION

Car Parking: 700 spaces at the ground – pre-bookings only. The club recommends all fans should use the free Matchday shuttle bus service which runs from Bruff Close, near Colchester North Railway Station where there is a large car park which can be used by Away fans.
Coach Parking: Drivers should liaise with with stewards upon arrival at the ground
Nearest Railway Station: Colchester North (1½ miles)
Nearest Bus Station: Colchester Town Centre (1½ miles)
Club Shop: At the ground
Opening Times: Monday to Friday 9.30am to 5.00pm. Saturday Non-Matchdays 10.00am to 2.00pm (until 3.00pm then after the game on Saturday Matchdays)
Telephone Nº: 0871 226-2161
Police Telephone Nº: (01206) 762212

GROUND INFORMATION

Away Supporters' Entrances & Sections: South Stand

ADMISSION INFO (2009/2010 PRICES)

Adult Seating: £20.00 – £26.00
Concessionary Seating: £13.00 – £19.00
Under-16s Seating: £8.00
Under-11s Seating: £5.00
Note: Additional concessionary rates are available in the Family Stand.
Programme Price: £3.00

DISABLED INFORMATION

Wheelchairs: 14 spaces in total situated in all stands with lift access available where required.
Helpers: One helper admitted per wheelchair
Prices: £22.00 for each adult disabled fan plus a helper. £15.00 for each concessionary disabled fan plus a helper.
Disabled Toilets: Available in each stand
Contact: 0845 437-9089 (Katy Springett – Bookings required)

Travelling Supporters' Information:
Routes: The stadium is located near the junction of the A12 and the A135 (Nayland Road) on the northern outskirts of Colchester. As parking at and near the stadium is very limited, the club recommends both home and away fans should use the Matchday shuttle bus service which runs from Bruff Close, near to Colchester North Station where there is a large car park.

COVENTRY CITY FC

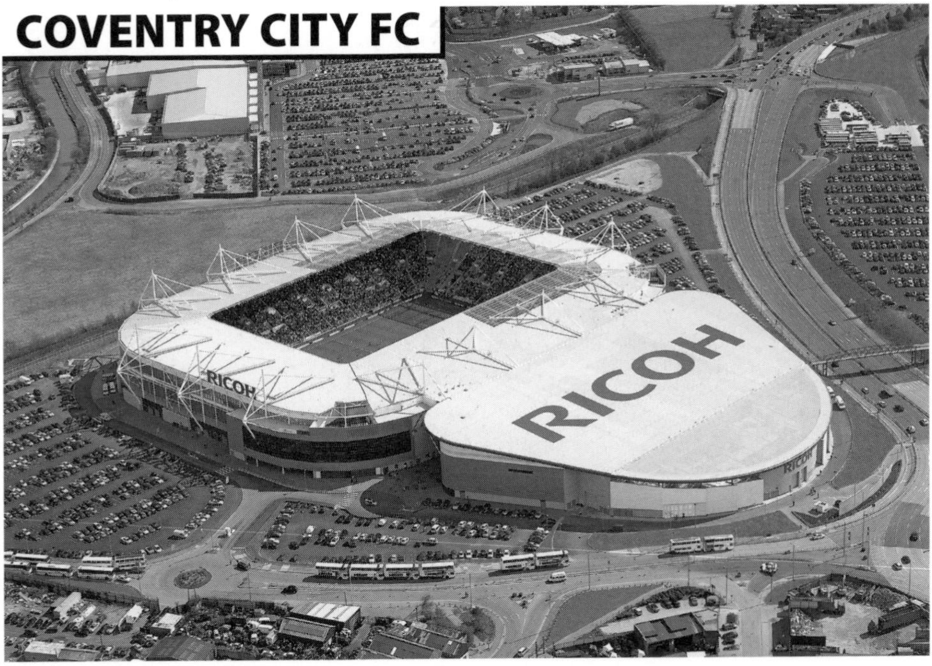

Founded: 1883 (Entered League: 1919)
Former Names: Singers FC (1883-1898)
Nickname: 'Sky Blues'
Ground: Ricoh Arena, Phoenix Way, Foleshill, Coventry CV6 6GE
Ground Capacity: 32,400 (All seats)
Record Attendance: 51,455 (At Highfield Road)
Pitch Size: 110 × 70 yards

Colours: Sky Blue shirts and socks, Navy Blue shorts
Telephone Nº: 0844 873-1883
Ticket Office: 0844 873-1883
Fax Numbers: 0870 421-1988 (General Office)
Web Site: www.ccfc.co.uk

GENERAL INFORMATION

Car Parking: 2,000 spaces available at the ground. Please pre-book parking via www.ricoharena.com or the ticket office
Coach Parking: At the ground (Car Park 'C')
Nearest Railway Station: Coventry (3 miles)
Nearest Bus Station: Coventry (3 miles)
Club Shop: At the ground
Opening Times: Weekday office hours and Matchdays
Telephone Nº: 0844 873-1883 (Option 2)
Police Telephone Nº: (024) 7653-9010

GROUND INFORMATION

Away Supporters' Entrances & Sections:
Turnstiles 1-11

ADMISSION INFO (2009/2010 PRICES)

Adult Seating: From £15.00
Child Seating: From £5.00
Programme Price: £3.00

DISABLED INFORMATION

Wheelchairs: 94 spaces available
Helpers: Admitted
Prices: From £8.00
Disabled Toilets: Available
Contact: 0844 873-1883 Option 2 (Bookings necessary)

Travelling Supporters' Information:
Routes: From All Parts: Exit the M6 at Junction 3 and follow the A444 towards Coventry. The ground is located just 400 yards along this road. Please note that parking spaces at the ground must be pre-booked. No street parking.

CREWE ALEXANDRA FC

Founded: 1877 (**Entered League:** 1892)
Nickname: 'Railwaymen'
Ground: Alexandra Stadium, Gresty Road, Crewe, Cheshire CW2 6EB
Ground Capacity: 10,107 (All seats)
Record Attendance: 20,000 (30th January 1960)
Pitch Size: 112 × 74 yards

Colours: Red shirts with White shorts
Telephone Nº: (01270) 213014
Ticket Office: (01270) 252610
Fax Number: (01270) 216320
Web Site: www.crewealex.net

GENERAL INFORMATION

Car Parking: Car Park at the ground (spaces for 400 cars)
Coach Parking: Car Park at the ground
Nearest Railway Station: Crewe (5 minutes walk)
Nearest Bus Station: Crewe Town
Club Shop: At the ground
Opening Times: Monday to Friday and Matchdays 9.00am – 5.00pm (until 7.45pm for Night matches)
Telephone Nº: (01270) 213014 extension 101
Police Telephone Nº: (01270) 500222

GROUND INFORMATION

Away Supporters' Entrances & Sections:
BMW Blue Bell Stand

ADMISSION INFO (2009/2010 PRICES)

Adult Seating: £19.00
Senior Citizen Seating: £15.00
Child Seating: £4.50 – £8.50
Programme Price: £2.50

DISABLED INFORMATION

Wheelchairs: Over 70 spaces available in total for home and away fans around the ground
Helpers: One helper admitted per disabled person
Prices: £15.00 for each disabled fan and helper
Disabled Toilets: Available in all Stands
Commentaries are available for the blind
Contact: (01270) 252610 (Bookings are necessary)

Travelling Supporters' Information:
Routes: From the North: Exit the M6 at Junction 17 and take the Crewe (A534) road, and at Crewe roundabout follow signs for Chester into Nantwich Road. Then take a left turn into Gresty Road; From the South and East: Take the A52 to the A5020, then on to Crewe roundabout (then as from the North); From the West: Take the A534 into Crewe and turn right just before the railway station into Gresty Road.

CRYSTAL PALACE FC

Founded: 1905 (**Entered League**: 1920)
Nickname: 'Eagles'
Ground: Selhurst Park, London SE25 6PU
Ground Capacity: 26,247 (All seats)
Record Attendance: 51,482 (11th May 1979)
Pitch Size: 110 × 74 yards

Colours: Red and Blue striped shirts with Red shorts
Telephone Nº: (020) 8768-6000
Ticket Office: 0871 200-0071
Fax Number: (020) 8771-5311
Web Site: www.cpfc.co.uk

GENERAL INFORMATION

Car Parking: Street Parking and in the Sainsburys Car Park near to the ground
Coach Parking: Thornton Heath
Nearest Railway Station: Selhurst or Norwood Junction (both 5 minutes walk)
Nearest Bus Station: West Croydon
Club Shop: At the ground
Opening Times: Weekdays & Matchdays 9.00am to 6.00pm
Telephone Nº: (020) 8768-6100
Police Telephone Nº: (020) 8768-1212

GROUND INFORMATION

Away Supporters' Entrances & Sections:
Park Road for the Arthur Wait Stand

ADMISSION INFO (2009/2010 PRICES)

Adult Seating: £21.50 – £34.50
Concessionary Seating: £14.50 – £19.50
Under-16s Seating: £9.50
Programme Price: £3.00

DISABLED INFORMATION

Wheelchairs: Spaces are available in the disabled area, Holmesdale Road Stand and also in the Arthur Wait Stand
Helpers: One helper admitted per wheelchair
Prices: Normal prices apply for the disabled. Helpers are admitted free of charge
Disabled Toilets: Located in the disabled section
Commentaries are available for 12 people
Contact: (020) 8768-6081 (Bookings are necessary)

Travelling Supporters' Information:
Routes: From the North: Take the M1/A1 to the North Circular (A406) for Chiswick. Take the South Circular (A205) to Wandsworth then the A3 to the A214 and follow signs for Streatham to the A23. Turn left onto the B273 after 1 mile, follow to the end, turn left into the High Street and then into Whitehorse Lane; From the East: Take the A232 (Croydon Road) to Shirley and join the A215 (Northwood Road). After 2¼ miles turn left into Whitehorse Lane; From the South: Take the A23 and follow signs for Crystal Palace (B266) through Thornton Heath into Whitehorse Lane; From the West: Take the M4 to Chiswick (then as North).

DAGENHAM & REDBRIDGE FC

Founded: 1992 (**Entered League**: 2007)
Former Names: Formed by the merger of Dagenham FC and Redbridge Forest FC
Nickname: 'The Daggers'
Ground: London Borough of Barking and Dagenham Stadium, Victoria Road, Dagenham RM10 7XL
Record Attendance: 7,100 (1967)
Pitch Size: 110 × 65 yards

Colours: Red and Blue shirts with White shorts
Telephone Nº: (020) 8592-1549
Office Phone Nº: (020) 8592-7194
Secretary's Phone Nº: (020) 8592-7194
Fax Number: (020) 8593-7227
Ground Capacity: 6,078
Seating Capacity: 1,015
Web site: www.daggers.co.uk

GENERAL INFORMATION

Supporters Club: Russell Elmes, 24 Brewood, Dagenham, RM8 2BL
Telephone Nº: (0208) 593-2801
Car Parking: Street parking only
Coach Parking: Street parking only
Nearest Railway Station: Dagenham East (5 mins. walk)
Nearest Bus Station: Romford
Club Shop: At the ground
Opening Times: Matchdays only
Telephone Nº: (020) 8592-7194
Police Telephone Nº: (020) 8593-8232

GROUND INFORMATION

Away Supporters' Entrances & Sections:
Pondfield Road entrances for Pondfield Road End

ADMISSION INFO (2009/2010 PRICES)

Adult Standing: £16.00
Adult Seating: £18.00 – £20.00
Under-16s Standing: £11.00
Child Seating: £10.00 – £14.00 (Under-7s £1.00 – £2.00)
Senior Citizen Seating: £10.00
Note: Discounts are available for advance purchases
Programme Price: £2.50

DISABLED INFORMATION

Wheelchairs: Accommodated in front of new Stand
Helpers: Admitted
Prices: £10.00 for the disabled. Free of charge for Helpers
Disabled Toilets: Available at the East and West ends of the ground and also in the Clubhouse
Contact: (020) 8592-7194 (Bookings are necessary)

Travelling Supporters' Information:
Routes: From the North & West: Take the M11 to its end and join the A406 South. At the large roundabout take the slip road on the left signposted A13 to Dagenham. As you approach Dagenham, stay in the left lane and follow signs for A1306 signposted Dagenham East. Turn left onto the A1112 at the 3rd set of traffic lights by the McDonalds. Proceed along Ballards Road to The Bull roundabout and bear left. Victoria Road is 450 yards on the left after passing Dagenham East tube station; From the South & East: Follow signs for the A13 to Dagenham. Take the next slip road off signposted Elm Park & Dagenham East then turn right at the roundabout. Go straight on at the next roundabout and turn left onto A1306. After ½ mile you will see a McDonalds on the right. Get into the right hand filter lane and turn right onto A1112. Then as from the North & West.

DARLINGTON FC

Founded: 1883 (**Entered League:** 1921)
Nickname: 'Quakers'
Ground: Darlington Arena, Hurworth Moor, Neasham Road, Darlington DL2 1DL
Ground Capacity: 25,321 (All seats)
Record Attendance: 10,224 (16th August 2003)
Pitch Size: 115 × 74 yards

Colours: White and Black shirts with Black shorts
Telephone Nº: (01325) 387000
Ticket Office: 0871 855-1883
Fax Number: (01325) 387050
Web Site: www.darlington-fc.net

GENERAL INFORMATION

Car Parking: Limited number of spaces at the ground
Coach Parking: At the ground
Nearest Railway Station: Darlington (1½ miles)
Nearest Bus Station: Darlington Central
Club Shop: At the ground
Opening Times: Monday to Friday 10.00am – 5.00pm and Saturday matchdays 10.00am – 3.00pm
Telephone Nº: (01325) 387020
Police Telephone Nº: (01325) 467681

GROUND INFORMATION

Away Supporters' Entrances & Sections:
East Stand

ADMISSION INFO (2009/2010 PRICES)

Adult Seating: £18.00
Senior Citizen/Student Seating: £12.00
Child Seating: £7.00 (Under-10s admitted free of charge)
Note: Price reductions are available if tickets are pre-booked
Programme Price: £2.50

DISABLED INFORMATION

Wheelchairs: Spaces available in disabled sections throughout the ground. Lifts are available in the stands
Helpers: One helper admitted per disabled person
Prices: £11.00 for the disabled and blind (£10.00 if purchased in advance). Free of charge for helpers
Disabled Toilets: Available in all stands
Contact: (01325) 387000 – Harry Sams

Travelling Supporters' Information:
Routes: From All Parts: Take the A1 to the A66(M) and follow the road to it's end.Take the 1st exit at the roundabout, go up the hill then, at the second roundabout, take the 3rd exit signposted A66 Teeside. The ground is at the next roundabout after approximately 1 mile.

DERBY COUNTY FC

Founded: 1884 (**Entered League**: 1888)
Nickname: 'Rams'
Ground: Pride Park Stadium, Royal Way, Pride Park, Derby DE24 8XL
Ground Capacity: 33,010 (All seats)
Record Attendance: 33,597 (25th May 2001)
Pitch Size: 110 × 74 yards

Colours: White shirts with Black shorts
Telephone Nº: 0871 472-1884
Ticket Office: 0871 472-1884
Fax Number: (01332) 667519
Web Site: www.dcfc.co.uk

GENERAL INFORMATION

Car Parking: Spaces for 1,424cars at the ground (permit holders only)
Coach Parking: At the ground
Nearest Railway Station: Derby Midland (1 mile)
Nearest Bus Station: Derby Central
Club Shop: shop dcfc at the ground
Opening Times: Monday to Saturday 9.00am – 5.00pm (from 10.00am on Tuesdays); Sundays 10.00am – 4.00pm
Telephone Nº: 0871 472-1884
Police Telephone Nº: (01332) 290100

GROUND INFORMATION

Away Supporters' Entrances & Sections: South Stand (Winfield Construction Stand)

ADMISSION INFO (2009/2010 PRICES)

Adult Seating: £21.50 – £36.00
Child Seating: £7.75 – £19.00
Concessionary Seating: £12.75 – £22.00
Note: Prices vary depending on the category of the game and tickets are cheaper if purchased before the matchday
Programme Price: £3.00

DISABLED INFORMATION

Wheelchairs: 206 spaces available in total
Helpers: One helper admitted for each disabled fan
Prices: £25.00 – £35.00 for each disabled fan & helper
Disabled Toilets: Yes
Contact: 0871 472-1884 (Bookings are necessary)

Travelling Supporters' Information:
Routes: From All Parts: Exit the M1 at Junction 25 and follow the A52 towards the City Centre until the ground is signposted on the left. Follow the signs for the ground.
From the Train Station: The Stadium is 10 minutes walk by way of a tunnel under the railway opposite Brunswick Inn, Station Approach. Then follow the footpath; Buses: A shuttle service runs from the bus station from 1.00pm until 2.45pm on Saturdays. A similar service runs from 6.00pm – 7.30pm for midweek games. Return shuttles are available post-match.

DONCASTER ROVERS FC

✓ OLD

Founded: 1879
Former Names: None
Nickname: 'Rovers'
Ground: Keepmoat Stadium, Stadium Way, Doncaster DN4 5JW
Record Attendance: 14,129 (6th January 2007)
Pitch Size: 110 × 72 yards

Colours: Red & White hooped shirts with Black shorts
Telephone Nº: (01302) 764664
Ticket Office: (01302) 762576
Fax Number: (01302) 363525
Ground Capacity: 15,231 (All seats)
Web site: www.doncasterroversfc.co.uk

GENERAL INFORMATION

Car Parking: 1,000 spaces available at the ground
Coach Parking: At the ground
Nearest Railway Station: Doncaster (2 miles)
Nearest Bus Station: Doncaster (2 miles)
Club Shop: At the ground
Opening Times: 10.00am to 4.30pm on weekdays and 10.00am to 4.00pm on Sundays
Telephone Nº: (01302) 764667
Police Telephone Nº: (01302) 366744

GROUND INFORMATION

Away Supporters' Entrances & Sections: North Stand

ADMISSION INFO (2009/2010 PRICES)

Adult Seating: £20.00 – £23.00
Child/Senior Citizen Seating: £13.00 – £17.00
Under-11s Seating: £5.00 – £10.00
Programme Price: £2.50
Note: Prices vary depending on the category of the game

DISABLED INFORMATION

Wheelchairs: Accommodated throughout the ground (Away fans accommodated in the North Stand)
Helpers: Admitted
Prices: Concessionary prices are charged for the disabled. Helpers are admitted free of charge
Disabled Toilets: Available in all Stands
Contact: (01302) 764664 (Bookings are necessary)

Travelling Supporters' Information:
Routes: Exit the M18 at Junction 3 and follow the A6182 towards Doncaster. The stadium is approximately 1½ miles from the motorway and is well signposted so follow these signs. There are 1,000 car parking spaces available at the stadium and the cost is £5.00 per car. A number of businesses on the nearby business park also offer matchday parking for a similar charge. When crowds over 9,000 are expected, a Park and Ride service runs from Doncaster Racecourse. The shuttle service buses run from 1.00pm to 3.00pm to the Stadium and from 4.30pm to 6.30pm returning to the Racecourse from the Stadium.

EVERTON FC

Founded: 1878 (**Entered League:** 1888)
Former Names: St. Domingo's FC (1878-79)
Nickname: 'The Toffees'
Ground: Goodison Park, Goodison Road, Liverpool L4 4EL
Ground Capacity: 40,565 (All seats)
Record Attendance: 78,299 (18th September 1948)
Pitch Size: 110 × 74 yards
Colours: Blue shirts with White shorts
Telephone Nº: 0870 442-1878
Ticket Office: 0870 442-1878
Fax Number: (0151) 286-9112
Web Site: www.evertonfc.com

GENERAL INFORMATION

Car Parking: Corner of Priory Road and Utting Avenue
Coach Parking: Priory Road
Nearest Railway Station: Kirkdale
Nearest Mainline Railway Station: Liverpool Lime Street
Nearest Bus Station: Queen's Square, Liverpool
Club Shop: 'Megastore' in Walton Lane by the ground
Opening Times: Weekdays 9.30am to 5.00pm, Wednesdays 10.00am to 5.00pm. Saturdays 9.00am to 5.00pm. Open one hour after matches
Telephone Nº: 0870 442-1878
Police Telephone Nº: (0151) 709-6010

GROUND INFORMATION

Away Supporters' Entrances & Sections:
Bullens Road entrances for Bullens Stand

ADMISSION INFO (2009/2010 PRICES)

Adult Seating: £29.00 – £35.00
Child Seating: £14.00 – £18.00
Senior Citizen Seating: £20.00 – £22.00
Note: Concessionary prices are only available in some areas and certain 'Premium' games are more expensive
Programme Price: £3.00

DISABLED INFORMATION

Wheelchairs: 85 spaces for home fans, 13 spaces for away fans in the disabled section.
Helpers: One helper admitted per wheelchair
Prices: £25.00 for each disabled fan + 1 helper
Disabled Toilets: Available in the disabled section
Commentaries are available for the blind
Contact: 0870 442-1878 (Bookings are necessary)

Travelling Supporters' Information:
Routes: From the North: Exit the M6 at Junction 26 onto the M58 and continue to it's end. Take the 2nd exit at the roundabout onto the A59 Ormskirk Road. Continue along into Rice Lane and go straight across at the next roundabout into County Road. After ½ mile, turn left into Everton Valley then bear left into Walton Lane for the ground; From the South & East: Exit the M6 at Junction 21A and take the M62 to it's end. Turn right at traffic lights onto A5088 Queen Drive and continue to the junction with Walton Hall Avenue then turn left into Walton Lane (A580) and the ground is on the right.
Bus Services: Services to the ground – 19, 20, F1, F2, 30

EXETER CITY FC

Founded: 1904 (**Re-Entered League:** 2008)
Former Names: Formed by the amalgamation of St. Sidwell United FC & Exeter United FC
Nickname: 'Grecians'
Ground: St. James Park, Exeter, EX4 6PX
Ground Capacity: 8,977
Seating Capacity: 3,806
Record Attendance: 20,984 (4th March 1931)

Pitch Size: 113 × 71 yards
Colours: Red and White striped shirts, Black shorts
Telephone Nº: (01392) 411243
Ticket Office: (01392) 411243
Fax Number: (01392) 413959
Web Site: www.exetercityfc.co.uk

GENERAL INFORMATION

Car Parking: King William Street
Coach Parking: Paris Street Bus Station
Nearest Railway Station: Exeter St. James Park (adjacent)
Nearest Bus Station: Paris Street Bus Station
Club Shop: At the ground
Opening Times: Weekdays 10.00am to 5.00pm and Matchdays from 10.00am until kick-off
Telephone Nº: (01392) 411243
Police Telephone Nº: 0990 700400

GROUND INFORMATION

Away Supporters' Entrances & Sections:
St. James Road turnstiles for standing in the St. James Road End or Well Street for seating in the Stagecoach Family Stand

ADMISSION INFO (2009/2010 PRICES)

Adult Standing: £15.00
Adult Seating: £17.00 – £20.00
Concessionary Standing: £10.00
Concessionary Seating: £12.00 – £14.00
Under-18s Standing: £5.00
Under-18s Seating: £6.00 – £14.00
Programme Price: £3.00

DISABLED INFORMATION

Wheelchairs: Accommodated in the Doble Stand and Cliff Bastin Stand
Helpers: One helper admitted per wheelchair
Prices: Free of charge for disabled. Normal prices for helpers
Disabled Toilets: Available by the Cliff Bastin Stand
Contact: (01392) 411243 (Bookings are necessary)

Travelling Supporters' Information:
Routes: From the North: Exit the M5 at Junction 30 and follow signs to the City Centre along Sidmouth Road and onto Heavitree Road. Take the 4th exit at the roundabout into Western Way and the 2nd exit into Tiverton Road then next left into St. James Road; From the East: Take the A30 into Heavitree Road (then as from the North); From the South & West: Take the A38 and follow City Centre signs into Western Way, then take the third exit at the roundabout into St. James Road.
Note: This ground is very difficult to find being in a residential area on the side of a hill without prominent floodlights.

FULHAM FC

Founded: 1879 (**Entered League**: 1907)
Former Names: Fulham St. Andrew's FC (1879-1898)
Nickname: 'Cottagers'
Ground: Craven Cottage, Stevenage Road, Fulham, London SW6 6HH
Ground Capacity: 26,600 (All seats)
Record Attendance: 49,335 (8th October 1938)

Pitch Size: 109 × 71 yards
Colours: White shirts with Black shorts
Telephone Nº: 0870 442-1222
Ticket Office: 0870 442-1234
Fax Number: (020) 7384-4810
Web Site: www.fulhamfc.com

GENERAL INFORMATION

Car Parking: Street Parking (Matchday restrictions apply)
Coach Parking: Stevenage Road/Fulham Palace Road
Nearest Railway Station: Putney (1 mile)
Nearest Tube Station: Putney Bridge (District) (1 mile)
Club Shop: At the ground and Fulham Road
Opening Times: At the ground: Weekends 12.00pm to 4.00pm, Matchdays with 3.00pm kick-off open 11.00am to 5.00pm; Evening Matches open 5.00pm to 10.00pm; Fulham Road: Monday to Saturday 9.00am to 5.00pm
Telephone Nº: 0870 442-1222
Police Telephone Nº: (020) 7385-1212

GROUND INFORMATION

Away Supporters' Entrances & Sections:
Putney End for the Putney Stand

ADMISSION INFO (2009/2010 PRICES)

Adult Seating: £25.00 – £55.00
Child Seating: £5.00 – £25.00
Concessionary Seating: £15.00 – £40.00
Note: Prices vary depending on the category of the game.
Programme Price: £3.50

DISABLED INFORMATION

Wheelchairs: 31 spaces for Home fans and 4 spaces for Away fans in the Putney End, Block 7
Helpers: One helper admitted per disabled person
Prices: Half-price for the disabled. Free of charge for helpers
Disabled Toilets: Available next to each disabled area
Contact: 0870 442-1234 Option 3 (Bookings necessary)

Travelling Supporters' Information:
Routes: From the North: Take the A1/M1 to the North Circular (A406), travel west to Neasden and follow signs for Harlesdon A404, then Hammersmith A219. At Broadway, follow the Fulham sign and turn right after 1 mile into Harboard Street then left at the end for the ground; From the South & East: Take the South Circular (A205), follow the Putney Bridge sign (A219). Cross the bridge and follow Hammersmith signs for ½ mile, turn left into Bishops Park Road, then right at the end; From the West: Take the M4 to the A4. Branch left after 2 miles into Hammersmith Broadway (then as from the North).

GILLINGHAM FC

Founded: 1893 (**Entered League:** 1920)
Former Names: New Brompton FC (1893-1913)
Nickname: 'Gills'
Ground: Priestfield Stadium, Redfern Avenue, Gillingham, Kent ME7 4DD
Ground Capacity: 11,500 (All seats)
Record Attendance: 23,002 (10th January 1948)
Pitch Size: 114 × 75 yards
Telephone Nº: (01634) 300000
Ticket Office: (01634) 300000 Option 3
Fax Number: (01634) 850986
Web Site: www.gillinghamfootballclub.com

GENERAL INFORMATION

Car Parking: Street parking
Coach Parking: By Police direction
Nearest Railway Station: Gillingham
Nearest Bus Station: Gillingham
Club Shop: Megastore in Redfern Avenue
Opening Times: Megastore is open Weekdays and Matchdays from 9.00am to 5.00pm
Telephone Nº: (01634) 300000
Police Telephone Nº: (01634) 891005

GROUND INFORMATION

Away Supporters' Entrances & Sections: Priestfield Road End

ADMISSION INFO (2009/2010 PRICES)

Adult Seating: £23.00
Senior Citizen Seating: £19.00
Under-22s Seating: £16.00
Under-16s Seating: £11.00
Under-11s Seating: £7.00
Note: Discounts are available for tickets purchased in advance
Programme Price: £2.50

DISABLED INFORMATION

Wheelchairs: 65 spaces in total for Home and Away fans and helpers in disabled sections around the ground
Helpers: One helper admitted per disabled person
Prices: Normal prices for the disabled. Free for helpers
Disabled Toilets: Available in the Gordon Road Stand
Contact: (01634) 300000 (Bookings are necessary)

Travelling Supporters' Information:
Routes: From All Parts: Exit the M2 at Junction 4 and follow the link road (dual carriageway) B278 to the 3rd roundabout. Turn left onto the A2 (dual carriageway) and go across the roundabout to the traffic lights. Turn right into Woodlands Road after the traffic lights. The ground is ¼ mile on the left.

GRIMSBY TOWN FC

Founded: 1878 (**Entered League**: 1892)
Former Names: Grimsby Pelham FC (1879)
Nickname: 'Mariners'
Ground: Blundell Park, Cleethorpes DN35 7PY
Ground Capacity: 8,974 (All seats)
Record Attendance: 31,651 (20th February 1937)
Pitch Size: 111 × 74 yards

Colours: Black and White striped shirts, Black shorts
Telephone Nº: (01472) 605050
Ticket Office: (01472) 605050
Fax Number: (01472) 693665
Web Site: www.gtfc.co.uk

GENERAL INFORMATION

Car Parking: Street parking
Coach Parking: Harrington Street – near the ground
Nearest Railway Station: Cleethorpes (1½ miles)
Nearest Bus Station: Brighowgate, Grimsby (4 miles)
Club Shop: At the ground
Opening Times: Monday – Friday 9.00am to 5.00pm; Matchday Saturdays 9.00am to kick-off
Telephone Nº: (01472) 605050
Police Telephone Nº: (01472) 359171

GROUND INFORMATION

Away Supporters' Entrances & Sections:
Harrington Street turnstiles 15-18 and Constitution Avenue turnstiles 5-14

ADMISSION INFO (2009/2010 PRICES)

Adult Seating: £18.00 (Away fans £18.00)
Senior Citizens/Young Adults (Ages 15–18): £12.00
Child Seating: £8.00 (Under-15s)
Programme Price: £2.50

DISABLED INFORMATION

Wheelchairs: 50 spaces in total for Home and Away fans in the disabled section, in front of the Main Stand
Helpers: Helpers are admitted
Prices: £18.00 for the disabled. Free of charge for helpers
Disabled Toilets: Available in disabled section
Commentaries are available in disabled section
Contact: (01472) 605050 (Bookings are necessary)

Travelling Supporters' Information:
Routes: From All Parts except Lincolnshire and East Anglia: Take the M180 to the A180 and follow signs for Grimsby/ Cleethorpes. The A180 ends at a roundabout (the 3rd in short distance after crossing docks), take the 2nd exit from the roundabout over the Railway flyover into Cleethorpes Road (A1098) and continue into Grimsby Road. After the second stretch of dual carriageway, the ground is ½ mile on the left; From Lincolnshire: Take the A46 or A16 and follow Cleethorpes signs along (A1098) Weelsby Road for 2 miles. Take the 1st exit at the roundabout at the end of Clee Road into Grimsby Road. The ground is 1¾ miles on the right.

HARTLEPOOL UNITED FC

Founded: 1908 (**Entered League:** 1921)
Former Names: Hartlepools United FC (1908-68); Hartlepool FC (1968-77)
Nickname: 'The Pool' 'Pools'
Ground: Victoria Park, Clarence Road, Hartlepool, TS24 8BZ
Ground Capacity: 7,787
Seating Capacity: 4,180
Record Attendance: 17,426 (15th January 1957)
Pitch Size: 110 × 74 yards
Colours: Shirts are White with Blue piping, Blue shorts
Telephone Nº: (01429) 272584
Ticket Office: (01429) 272584 Extension 2
Ticket Office e-mail: tickets@hartlepoolunited.co.uk
Fax Number: (01429) 863007
Web Site: www.hartlepoolunited.co.uk

GENERAL INFORMATION

Car Parking: Limited space at the ground (£8.00 charge) and also street parking
Coach Parking: Church Street
Nearest Railway Station: Hartlepool Church Street (5 minutes walk)
Club Shop: At the ground
Opening Times: Weekdays 9.00am to 5.00pm; non-match Saturdays 9.00am to 1.00pm. Saturday matchdays 10.00am–3.00pm and 4.30pm–5.30pm
Telephone Nº: (01429) 260491
Police Telephone Nº: (01429) 221151

GROUND INFORMATION

Away Supporters' Entrances & Sections: Clarence Road turnstiles 1 & 2 for Rink End

ADMISSION INFO (2009/2010 PRICES)

Adult Standing: £18.00
Adult Seating: £20.00
Child/Senior Citizen Standing: £9.00
Child/Senior Citizen Seating: £10.00 (£8.00 Family Stand)
Programme Price: £2.50

DISABLED INFORMATION

Wheelchairs: 21 spaces for Home fans in disabled section, Cyril Knowles Stand, 10 spaces for Away fans in the Rink End
Helpers: One helper admitted per wheelchair
Prices: £20.00 for the Disabled. Helpers free of charge
Disabled Toilets: Available in the Cyril Knowles Stand
Contact: (01429) 272584 (Bookings are advisable)

Travelling Supporters' Information: Routes: From the North: Take the A1/A19 to the A179 and follow Town Centre/Marina signs. Turn right at the roundabout by the 'Historic Quayside' and cross over the Railway bridge. The ground is on the left; From the South & West: Take the A689 following Town Centre/Marina signs. Turn left at the roundabout by the 'Historic Quayside' and cross over the Railway bridge. The ground is on the left.

HEREFORD UNITED FC

Founded: 1924
Former Names: None
Nickname: 'United' 'The Bulls'
Ground: Edgar Street, Hereford HR4 9JU
Record Attendance: 18,114 (4th January 1958)
Pitch Size: 112 × 78 yards

Colours: White shirts with White shorts
Telephone Nº: (01432) 276666
Fax Number: (01432) 341359
Ground Capacity: 7,873
Seating Capacity: 2,761
Web site: www.herefordunited.co.uk

GENERAL INFORMATION

Supporters Club: None
Car Parking: Merton Meadow Car Park
Coach Parking: Cattle Market (Near the ground)
Nearest Railway Station: Hereford (½ mile)
Nearest Bus Station: Commercial Road, Hereford
Club Shop: At the ground
Opening Times: Weekdays 9.00am to 4.00pm and Matchdays 12.00pm to 3.00pm
Telephone Nº: (01432) 276666
Police Telephone Nº: (01432) 276422

GROUND INFORMATION

Away Supporters' Entrances & Sections:
Blackfriars Street and Edgar Street for the Blackfriars Street End

ADMISSION INFO (2009/2010 PRICES)

Adult Standing: £13.00
Adult Seating: £15.00
Child Standing: £9.00 (Junior Bulls £4.00)
Child Seating: £12.00 (Junior Bulls £4.00)
Under-10s: £3.00 (Advance purchases only)
Senior Citizen Standing: £9.00
Senior Citizen Seating: £12.00
Programme Price: £2.50

DISABLED INFORMATION

Wheelchairs: 10 spaces in total for Home and Away fans in the disabled section, Merton Meadow Stand
Helpers: One helper admitted per disabled person
Prices: £12.00 for the disabled. Free of charge for helpers
Disabled Toilets: Yes
Contact: (01432) 276666 (Bookings are not necessary)

Travelling Supporters' Information:
Routes: From the North: Follow A49 Hereford signs straight into Edgar Street; From the East: Take the A465 or A438 into Hereford Town Centre, then follow signs for Leominster (A49) into Edgar Street; From the South: Take the A49 or A45 into the Town Centre (then as East); From the West: Take the A438 into the Town Centre (then as East).

HUDDERSFIELD TOWN FC

Founded: 1908 (**Entered League:** 1910)
Nickname: 'Terriers'
Ground: The Galpharm Stadium, Huddersfield, HD1 6PX
Ground Capacity: 24,554 (All seats)
Record Attendance: 23,678 (12th December 1999)
Pitch Size: 115 × 76 yards

Colours: Blue and White striped shirts, White shorts and Blue socks
Telephone Nº: 0870 444-4677
Ticket Office: 0870 444-4552
Fax Number: (01484) 484101
Web Site: www.htafc.com

GENERAL INFORMATION

Car Parking: Car park for 1,100 cars adjacent (pre-sold)
Coach Parking: Adjacent car park
Nearest Railway Station: Huddersfield (1¼ miles)
Nearest Bus Station: Huddersfield
Club Shop: At the ground and in the Town Centre
Opening Times: Weekdays 9.00am to 5.00pm, Saturday Matchdays 9.00am to 3.00pm and Saturday Non-matchdays 9.00am to 12.00pm
Telephone Nº: (01484) 484144 or 421612
Police Telephone Nº: (01484) 422122

GROUND INFORMATION

Away Supporters' Entrances & Sections:
Pink Link Stand

ADMISSION INFO (2009/2010 PRICES)

Adult Seating: £19.00 – £27.00
Child Seating: £5.00 – £12.00
Senior Citizen/Student Seating: £10.00 – £19.00
Programme Price: £3.00

DISABLED INFORMATION

Wheelchairs: 254 spaces in total for home and away fans in the disabled sections, Direct Golf UK Lower Stand, Pink Link Stand and Antich Stand. Additional spaces are available for the ambulant disabled and visually impaired.
Helpers: Admitted
Prices: £11.00 – £27.00 for the disabled. Free of charge for helpers
Disabled Toilets: Available in the disabled sections
Commentaries are available for the blind.
Contact: 0870 444-4552 (Bookings are necessary)

Travelling Supporters' Information:
Routes: From the North, East and West: Exit the M62 at Junction 25 and take the A644 and A62 following Huddersfield signs. Follow signs for the Galpharm Stadium; From the South: Leave the M1 at Junction 38 and follow the A637/A642 to Huddersfield. At the Ring Road, follow signs for the A62 to the Galpharm Stadium.

HULL CITY AFC

Founded: 1904 (**Entered League**: 1905)
Nickname: 'Tigers'
Ground: The Kingston Communications Stadium, The Circle, Walton Street, Hull HU3 6HU
Ground Capacity: 25,567 (All seats)
Record Attendance: 24,945 (24th May 2009)
Pitch Size: 115 × 75 yards

Colours: Black and Amber shirts with Black shorts
Telephone Nº: (01482) 504600
Ticket Office: (01482) 505600
Fax Number: (01482) 304882
Web Site: www.hullcityafc.net

GENERAL INFORMATION

Car Parking: Walton Street Car Park (£5.00), City Centre Car Parks and a Park & Ride scheme from Priory Park (£1.20)
Coach Parking: By Police direction
Nearest Railway Station: Hull Interchange
Nearest Bus Station: City Centre, Hull
Club Shop: Tiger Leisure Superstore at the Stadium
Opening Times: Monday to Saturday 9.00am to 5.00pm. Open until 5.30pm on Saturday matchdays
Telephone Nº: (01482) 509600
Police Telephone Nº: (01482) 220148

GROUND INFORMATION

Away Supporters' Entrances & Sections:
North Stand

ADMISSION INFO (2009/2010 PRICES)

Adult Seating: £24.50
Concessionary Seating: £14.50
Programme Price: £3.00

DISABLED INFORMATION

Wheelchairs: 304 spaces in total for Home and Away fans available around all the stands at both upper and lower level
Helpers: One helper admitted per disabled person (subject to registration)
Prices: Concessionary rates for the disabled. Free for helpers
Disabled Toilets: Many available throughout the ground. Lifts are available. Commentaries are available for the blind
Contact: (01482) 504600 (Bookings are not necessary)

Travelling Supporters' Information:
Routes: From the West: Take the M62 then join the A63. Continue under the Humber Bridge as the road becomes the A63 Clive Sullivan Way and turn off at the slip road just before the flyover marked "Local Traffic/Infirmary". Take the 2nd exit at the roundabout into Rawling Way. Turn left at the next main set of traffic lights on A1105 Anlaby Road. Continue over the flyover then take a right turn into Walton Street. The car park is half way down this street after the Sports Arena; From the Humber Bridge: Follow signs for Hull City Centre – the road curves round to the left to join the A63 Clive Sullivan Way. Then as from the West; From the North: Take the A1079 towards Beverley then follow signs for the Humber Bridge and A164. Take the A63 sign-posted Hull City Centre and follow onto the A63 Clive Sullivan Way. Then as from the West.

IPSWICH TOWN FC

Founded: 1878 (**Entered League:** 1938)
Nickname: 'Town' 'Tractor Boys'
Ground: Portman Road, Ipswich IP1 2DA
Ground Capacity: 30,311 (All seats)
Record Attendance: 38,010 (8th March 1975)
Pitch Size: 112 × 72 yards

Colours: Blue shirts with White shorts
Telephone Nº: (01473) 400500
Ticket Office: 0870 111-0555
Fax Number: (01473) 400040
Web Site: www.itfc.co.uk

GENERAL INFORMATION

Car Parking: Portman Road & Sir Alf Ramsey Way car parks
Coach Parking: Bibb Way
Nearest Railway Station: Ipswich (5 minutes walk)
Nearest Bus Station: Ipswich
Club Shop: At the ground
Opening Times: Weekdays 8.30am–5.00pm. Opening times on Matchdays vary. Please contact the club for details
Telephone Nº: (01473) 400501
Police Telephone Nº: (01473) 613500

GROUND INFORMATION

Away Supporters' Entrances & Sections:
Cobbold Stand

ADMISSION INFO (2009/2010 PRICES)

Adult Seating: £26.50 – £51.50
Child Seating: £7.00 – £25.50
Senior Citizen Seating: £19.00 – £39.00
Note: Discounts are available for advance ticket purchases.
Programme Price: £3.00

DISABLED INFORMATION

Wheelchairs: 120 spaces and 130 seats for home fans, 10 spaces and 10 seats for away fans in the Britannia, Greene King and North Stands upper and lower tiers
Helpers: One helper admitted per disabled person
Prices: Adult price charged for disabled fan + one helper.
Disabled Toilets: Adjacent to the disabled areas
Commentaries are available for the blind
Contact: 0870 111-0555 (Bookings are necessary)

Travelling Supporters' Information:
Routes: From the North and West: Take the A1214 from the A14/A12 following signs for Ipswich West only. Proceed through Holiday Inn Hotel traffic lights and at the 3rd set of traffic lights turn right into West End Road. The ground is ¼ mile along on the left; From the South: Follow signs for Ipswich West, then as from the North and West above.

LEEDS UNITED FC

Founded: 1919 (**Entered League**: 1920)
Former Names: Formed after Leeds City FC were wound up for 'Irregular Practices'
Nickname: 'United'
Ground: Elland Road, Leeds LS11 0ES
Ground Capacity: 39,460 (All seats)
Record Attendance: 57,892 (15th March 1967)
Pitch Size: 115 × 74 yards
Colours: White shirts and shorts
Telephone N°: (0113) 367-6000
Ticket Office: 0845 121-1992
Fax Number: (0113) 367-6050
Web Site: www.leedsunited.com

GENERAL INFORMATION

Car Parking: Large car parks adjacent to the Stadium
Coach Parking: Adjacent to the Stadium
Nearest Railway Station: Leeds City (1½ miles)
Nearest Bus Station: Leeds City Centre – specials from Swinegate
Club Shop: At the South East corner of the Stadium
Opening Times: Weekdays 9.00am to 5.00pm, Matchdays 9.00am to one hour after the final whistle
Telephone N°: (0113) 367-6221
Police Telephone N°: 0845 6060606

GROUND INFORMATION

Away Supporters' Entrances & Sections:
South East Corner or South Stand – Upper & Lower Tiers

ADMISSION INFO (2009/2010 PRICES)

Adult Seating: £15.00 – £31.00
Child Seating: £7.00 – £12.00 (£7.00 in Family Stand)
Senior Citizen Seating: £11.00 – £16.00
Note: Prices vary according to the category of game played.
Programme Price: £3.00

DISABLED INFORMATION

Wheelchairs: 131 spaces in total in the disabled sections, West, North and South Stands
Helpers: One helper admitted per disabled person
Prices: Please contact the club for details
Disabled Toilets: Adjacent to each of the disabled sections
Commentaries via headphones in the West Stand
Contact: (0113) 367-6178 (Ms. Tracey Lazenby)
(Bookings are necessary)

Travelling Supporters' Information:
Routes: From the North: Take the A58 or A61 into the City Centre and follow signs to the M621. Leave the Motorway after 1½ miles and exit the roundabout onto the A643 into Elland Road; From the North-East: Take the A63 or A64 into the City Centre (then as from the North); From the South: Take the M1 to the M621 (then as from the North); From the West: Take the M62 to the M621 (then as from the North).

LEICESTER CITY FC

Founded: 1884 (**Entered League**: 1894)
Former Names: Leicester Fosse FC (1884-1919)
Nickname: 'Foxes'
Ground: Walkers Stadium, Filbert Way, Leicester, LE2 7FL
Ground Capacity: 32,500 (All seats)
Record Attendance: 32,148 (26th December 2003)
Pitch Size: 110 × 72 yards
Colours: Blue shirts and shorts
Telephone N°: 0844 815-6000
Ticket Office: 0844 815-5000
Fax Number: (0116) 229-4404
Web Site: www.lcfc.com

GENERAL INFORMATION

Car Parking: NCP Car Park (5 minutes walk)
Coach Parking: Sawday Street
Nearest Railway Station: Leicester (1 mile)
Nearest Bus Station: St. Margaret's (1 mile)
Club Shop: At the ground
Opening Times: Monday to Saturday 9.00am–5.00pm. Saturday Matchdays open 9.00am until kick-off then for 30 minutes after the game. Sundays open 10.00am – 4.00pm
Telephone N°: 0844 815-6000
Police Telephone N°: (0116) 222-2222

GROUND INFORMATION

Away Supporters' Entrances & Sections:
At the corner of the North and East Stands

ADMISSION INFO (2009/2010 PRICES)

Adult Seating: £23.00 – £32.00
Under-8s Seating: £3.00 (Free in the North Stand)
Under-16s Seating: £10.00 **Under-12s Seating**: £5.00
Under-22s/Student Seating: £15.00
Senior Citizen Seating: £21.00
Note: Various discounts are available for members
Programme Price: £3.00

DISABLED INFORMATION

Wheelchairs: 186 spaces for the disabled + 111 spaces for helpers accommodated at various levels in all stands
Helpers: One carer admitted per disabled person
Prices: Reduced prices are available – Phone for details
Disabled Toilets: Available in all stands
Contact: 0844 815-5000 (Hayley Mason – phone or fax)

Travelling Supporters' Information:
Routes: From the North: Take the A46/A607 into the City Centre or exit the M1 at Junction 21, take the A5460, turn right ¾ mile after the Railway Bridge into Upperton Road, then right into Filbert Way; From the East: Take the A47 into the City Centre (then as from the North); From the South: Exit the M1 at Junction 21 and take the A5460, turn right ¾ mile after Railway Bridge into Upperton Road, then right into Filbert Way; From the West: Take the M69 to the City Centre (then as from North).

LEYTON ORIENT FC

Founded: 1881 (**Entered League**: 1905)
Former Names: Glyn Cricket and Football Club (1881-86); Eagle FC (1886-88); Clapton Orient FC (1888-1946); Leyton Orient FC (1946-66); Orient FC (1966-87)
Nickname: 'O's'
Ground: Matchroom Stadium, Brisbane Road, Leyton, London E10 5NF
Ground Capacity: 9,311 (all seats)
Record Attendance: 34,345 (21st January 1964)
Pitch Size: 110 × 76 yards
Telephone Nº: 0871 310-1881
Ticket Office: 0871 310-1883
Fax Number: 0871 310-1882
Web Site: www.leytonorient.com

GENERAL INFORMATION

Car Parking: Street parking
Coach Parking: By Police direction
Nearest Railway Station: Leyton Midland Road (½ mile)
Nearest Tube Station: Leyton (Central)
Club Shop: At the ground
Opening Times: Weekdays 9.30am to 4.30pm
Telephone Nº: 0871 310-1889
Police Telephone Nº: (020) 8556-8855

GROUND INFORMATION

Away Supporters' Entrances & Sections:
East Stand

ADMISSION INFO (2008/2009 PRICES)

Adult Seating: £20.00 – £35.00
Child Seating: £5.00 in the North Family Stand only – free of charge for Under-11s if booked in advance
Senior Citizen Seating: £13.00 – £25.00
Programme Price: £3.00

DISABLED INFORMATION

Wheelchairs: Spaces are available in the North, East and West Stands
Helpers: One helper admitted per disabled person
Prices: Free of charge for the disabled and helpers
Disabled Toilets: Available near disabled sections
Contact: 0871 310-1883 (Bookings are necessary)

Travelling Supporters' Information:
Routes: From the North & West: Take A406 North Circular, follow signs for Chelmsford to Edmonton. After 2½ miles take the 3rd exit at the roundabout towards Leyton (A112). Pass the railway station, turn right after ½ mile into Windsor Road and left into Brisbane Road; From the East: Follow the A12 to London then the City for Leytonstone. Follow Hackney signs into Grove Road, cross Main Road into Ruckholt Road then turn right into Leyton High Road, turn left after ¼ mile into Buckingham Road and left into Brisbane Road; From the South: Take the A102M through the Blackwall Tunnel, follow signs for Newmarket (A102) to join the A11 to Stratford, then follow signs for Stratford Station into Leyton Road to the railway station (then as from North).

LINCOLN CITY FC

Founded: 1884 (Entered League: 1892)
Nickname: 'Red Imps'
Ground: Sincil Bank Stadium, Lincoln LN5 8LD
Ground Capacity: 10,120 (All seats)
Record Attendance: 23,196 (15th November 1967)
Pitch Size: 110 × 72 yards

Colours: Red and White striped shirts, Black shorts
Telephone Nº: 0870 899-2005
Ticket Office: 0870 899-1976
Fax Number: (01522) 880020
Web Site: www.redimps.com

GENERAL INFORMATION

Car Parking: Stacey West Car Park (limited parking for £5.00 per car).
Coach Parking: Please contact the club for details.
Nearest Railway Station: Lincoln Central
Club Shop: At the ground
Opening Times: Weekdays 9.00am to 5.00pm and Saturday Matchdays 10.00am to 5.00pm
Telephone Nº: 0870 899-2005
Police Telephone Nº: (01522) 529911

GROUND INFORMATION

Away Supporters' Entrances & Sections:
Lincolnshire Co-operative Stand (seated) – Turnstiles 19-23

ADMISSION INFO (2009/2010 PRICES)

Adult Seating: £16.00 – £18.00
Child Seating: £6.00
Concessionary Seating: £10.00 – £12.00
Note: Prices vary depending on the category of the game and discounts are available for advance ticket purchases
Programme Price: £2.50

DISABLED INFORMATION

Wheelchairs: Limited number of spaces available in the disabled section, adjacent to turnstile 23
Helpers: One helper admitted per disabled person
Prices: Applications for disabled passes must be made to the club. Wheelchair-bound disabled are charged concessionary prices. Helpers are admitted free if the disabled fan has a medium/high level disability allowance
Disabled Toilets: Adjacent to disabled area
Contact: 0870 899-2005 (Bookings are necessary)

Travelling Supporters' Information:
Routes: From the East: Take the A46 or A158 into the City Centre following Newark (A46) signs into the High Street and take next left (Scorer Street and Cross Street) for the ground; From the North and West: Take the A15 or A57 into the City Centre, then as from the East; From the South: Take the A1 then A46 for the City Centre, then into the High Street, parking on the South Common or in the Stadium via South Park Avenue, turn down by the Fire Station.

LIVERPOOL FC

Founded: 1892 (**Entered League:** 1893)
Nickname: 'Reds'
Ground: Anfield Road, Liverpool L4 0TH
Ground Capacity: 45,362 (All seats)
Record Attendance: 61,905 (2nd February 1952)
Pitch Size: 111 × 74 yards

Colours: Red shirts, shorts and socks
Telephone Nº: (0151) 263-2361
Ticket Office: 0844 844-0844
Ticket Office Fax Number: (0151) 261-1416
Customer Services: 0844 844-2005
General Fax Number: (0151) 260-8813
Web Site: www.liverpoolfc.tv

GENERAL INFORMATION

Car Parking: None available in the immediate area
Coach Parking: Priory Road and Pinehurst Avenue
Nearest Railway Station: Kirkdale (¾ mile)
Nearest Bus Station: Paradise Street, Liverpool
Club Shop: At the ground, at Williamson Square and 'Liverpool One' in the City Centre and in Chester City Centre
Opening Times: At Anfield: Monday to Friday 9.00am to 5.00pm, Saturdays 9.30am to 4.00pm; At Williamson Square and Chester: Monday to Friday 9.00am to 5.30pm; At Liverpool One: Monday to Friday 9.30am to 8.00pm, Saturdays 9.00am – 7.00pm and Sundays 11.00am – 5.00pm
Telephone Nº: (0151) 263-2361

GROUND INFORMATION

Away Supporters' Entrances & Sections:
Anfield Road

ADMISSION INFO (2009/2010 PRICES)

Adult Seating: £37.00 – £39.00
Adult Kop Seating: £35.00 – £37.00
Senior Citizen Seating: £28.00 – £29.50
Senior Citizen Kop Seating: £26.00 – £28.00
Note: Combined Adult/Child tickets are also available
Programme Price: £3.00

DISABLED INFORMATION

Wheelchairs: 79 spaces available in total in the Paddock Enclosure, Kop Stand and Anfield Road Stand
Helpers: One helper admitted per wheelchair
Prices: £26.00 – £29.50 the disabled. Helpers are admitted free of charge
Disabled Toilets: Two available in the Paddock, two in the Kop Stand and one in the Anfield Road Stand
Commentaries are available for the visually impaired on request
Contact: 0844 844-2005 (Bookings are necessary)

Travelling Supporters' Information:
Routes: From the North: Exit the M6 at Junction 28 and follow Liverpool A580 signs into Walton Hall Avenue, pass Stanley Park and turn left into Anfield Road; From the South and East: Take the M62 to the end of the motorway, then turn right into Queen's Drive (A5058) and turn left after 3 miles into Utting Avenue. After 1 mile, turn right into Anfield Road; From North Wales: Take the Mersey Tunnel into the City Centre and follow signs for Preston (A580) into Walton Hall Avenue. Turn right into Anfield Road before Stanley Park.

MACCLESFIELD TOWN FC

Founded: 1874 (**Entered League:** 1997)
Former Names: Macclesfield FC
Nickname: 'The Silkmen'
Ground: Moss Rose Ground, London Road, Macclesfield, Cheshire SK11 7SP
Ground Capacity: 6,141
Seating Capacity: 2,520
Record Attendance: 10,041 (1948)

Pitch Size: 110 × 72 yards
Colours: Blue shirts, White shorts and Blue socks
Telephone Nº: (01625) 264686
Ticket Office: (01625) 264686
Fax Number: (01625) 264692
Web Site: www.mtfc.co.uk

GENERAL INFORMATION

Car Parking: Ample parking available near the ground
Coach Parking: Near the ground
Nearest Railway Station: Macclesfield (1 mile)
Nearest Bus Station: Macclesfield
Club Shop: At the ground
Opening Times: Weekdays and matchdays 9.00am to 5.00pm
Telephone Nº: (01625) 264686
Police Telephone Nº: (01625) 610000

GROUND INFORMATION

Away Supporters' Entrances & Sections:
Silkman Terrace and the left side of the McAlpine Stand

ADMISSION INFO (2009/2010 PRICES)

Adult Standing: £14.00
Adult Seating: £18.00
Concessions Standing: £10.00
Concessions Seating: £14.00
Under-12s Standing/Seating: Free with a paying adult
Ages 12-15 Standing/Seating: £5.00
Adult Hospitality Package: £39.50
Programme Price: £2.50

DISABLED INFORMATION

Wheelchairs: 45 spaces in front of the Estate Road Stand
Helpers: One helper admitted per disabled fan
Prices: Concessionary prices apply for disabled and helpers
Disabled Toilets: 3 available
Contact: (01625) 264686 (Bookings are necessary)

Travelling Supporters' Information:
Routes: From the North: Exit the M6 at Junction 19 to Knutsford, follow the A537 to Macclesfield. Follow signs for the Town Centre, then for the A523 to Leek. The ground is 1 mile out of the Town Centre on the right; From the South: Exit M6 at Junction 17 for Sandbach and follow the A534 to Congleton. Then take the A536 to Macclesfield. After passing The Rising Sun on the left, ¼ mile further on turn right after the Texaco Garage (Moss Lane). Following this lane will bring you back to the ground.

MANCHESTER CITY FC

Founded: 1887 (**Entered League**: 1892)
Former Name: Ardwick FC (1887-1894)
Nickname: 'Citizens' 'City' 'Blues'
Ground: City of Manchester Stadium, SportCity, Manchester M11 3FF
Ground Capacity: 47,200 (All seats)
Record Attendance: 47,304 (vs Chelsea – 2004)
Pitch Size: 115 × 75 yards

Colours: Sky Blue shirtswith White shorts
Telephone Nº: 0870 062-1894
Ticket Office: 0870 062-1894
Credit Card Bookings: 0870 062-1894
Fax Number: (0161) 438-7999
Web Site: www.mcfc.co.uk

GENERAL INFORMATION

Car Parking: 1,000 spaces available at the stadium. Another 7,000 spaces are available off site in the vicinity.
Coach Parking: Around 40 spaces available at the stadium
Nearest Railway Station: Ashburys (15 minutes walk) or Manchester Piccadilly (20 minutes walk)
Nearest Bus Station: 53, 54, 185, 216, 217, 230, 231, 232, 233, 234, 235, 236, 137, X36, X37 services all stop at the stadium
Club Shop: At the stadium
Opening Times: Monday to Saturday 9.00am – 5.30pm, Matchdays 9.00am – 6.00pm, Sundays 11.00am – 4.00pm
Telephone Nº: 0870 062-1894
Police Telephone Nº: (0161) 872-5050

GROUND INFORMATION

Away Supporters' Entrances & Sections: South Stand

ADMISSION INFO (2009/2010 PRICES)

Adult Seating: £23.00 – £38.00
Child Seating: £10.00
Senior Citizen Seating: £11.00 – £22.00
Note: Prices vary depending on the category of the game and discounts are available for tickets purchased in advance
Programme Price: £3.00

DISABLED INFORMATION

Wheelchairs: Around 200 spaces available in total
Helpers: One helper admitted per wheelchair
Prices: £14.00 – £21.00 per disabled fan
Disabled Toilets: Available in all stands
Commentaries for the blind and lifts are also available
Contact: (0161) 438-7747 (Bookings are recommended)

Travelling Supporters' Information:
Routes: From the North: Exit the M60 at Junction 23 onto the A662 Ashton New Road. The stadium is approximately 1½ miles on the right hand side; From the East: Take the A635 which becomes the A662 Ashton New Road. Then as from the North; From the South: Take the M56 onto the M60. Join the A34 Kingsway at Junction 3. Follow the A34 until you join the A6010 Alan Turing Way. The Stadium is situated on the left, after approximately 2½ miles; From the West: Take the M61 to the M60. Exit at Junction 23, then follow directions as from the North.

MANCHESTER UNITED FC

Founded: 1878 (**Entered League**: 1892)
Former Names: Newton Heath LYR FC (1878-1892), Newton Heath FC (1892-1902)
Nickname: 'Red Devils'
Ground: Sir Matt Busby Way, Old Trafford, Manchester M16 0RA
Ground Capacity: 76,022 (All seats)
Record Attendance: 76,962 (25th March 1939)

Pitch Size: 115 × 76 yards
Colours: Red shirts with White shorts
Telephone Nº: (0161) 868-8000
Ticket Information: (0161) 868-8000
Fax Number: (0161) 868-8804
Web Site: www.manutd.com

GENERAL INFORMATION

Car Parking: Lancashire Cricket Ground and Car Park E3 on John Gilbert Way. Other approved car parks are signposted
Coach Parking: By Police direction
Nearest Railway Station: At the ground
Nearest Bus Station: Chorlton Street
Nearest Metro Station: Old Trafford, located at L.C.C.C. and also Salford Quays
Club Shop: At the ground
Opening Times: Weekdays 9.00am – 5.30pm; Matchdays 9.00am to kick-off + 1 hour after match; Sundays 10.30am – 4.30pm; Non-match Saturdays 9.00am – 5.00pm
Telephone Nº: (0161) 868-8000
Museum & Tour Centre: (0161) 868-8000
Police Telephone Nº: (0161) 872-5050

GROUND INFORMATION

Away Supporters' Entrances & Sections:
South Stand (turnstile 22) & East Stand (turnstile 30)

ADMISSION INFO (2009/2010 PRICES)

Adult Seating: £27.00 – £49.00
Senior Citizen Seating: £13.50 – £20.00
Under-16s Seating: £10.00 (Members only)
Programme Price: £3.00

DISABLED INFORMATION

Wheelchairs: 104 spaces in total for Home and Away fans in the disabled section – in front of 'L' Stand
Helpers: One helper admitted per disabled person
Prices: Free of charge for the disabled and helpers
Disabled Toilets: Located near the disabled section
Commentaries are available for the visually impaired
Contact: (0161) 868-8000 (Bookings are necessary)

Travelling Supporters' Information:
Routes: From the North and West: Take the M61 to the M60 and exit at Junction 4 following Manchester (A5081) signs. Turn right after 2½ miles into Sir Matt Busby Way for the ground; From the South: Exit the M6 at Junction 19 and take Stockport (A556) road then Altrincham (A56). From Altrincham follow Manchester signs and turn left into Sir Matt Busby Way after 6 miles; From the East: Exit the M62 at Junction 17 and take the A56 to Manchester. Follow signs for the South then signs for Chester (Chester Road). Turn right into Sir Matt Busby Way after 2 miles.

MIDDLESBROUGH FC

Founded: 1876 (Entered League: 1899)
Nickname: 'Boro'
Ground: Riverside Stadium, Middlesbrough, TS3 6RS
Ground Capacity: 34,998 (All seats)
Record Attendance: 34,836 (28th December 2004)
Pitch Size: 115 × 75 yards

Colours: Red shirts and shorts
Telephone Nº: 0844 499-6789
Ticket Office: 0844 499-1234
Fax Number: (01642) 757697
Web Site: www.mfc.co.uk

GENERAL INFORMATION

Car Parking: 1,250 spaces (Season Car Park passes only)
Coach Parking: At the ground
Nearest Railway Station: Middlesbrough (½ mile)
Nearest Bus Station: Middlesbrough
Club Shops: At ground and Captain Cook Square
Opening Times: Weekdays 9.30am – 5.00pm and Saturday Matchdays 9.30am until kick-off; Captain Cook Square: Monday to Saturday 9.00am – 5.30pm
Telephone Nº: 0844 499-2676 (Ground); (01642) 877849 (Captain Cook Square)
Police Telephone Nº: (01642) 248184

GROUND INFORMATION

Away Supporters' Entrances & Sections:
South Stand turnstiles for the South Stand

ADMISSION INFO (2009/2010 PRICES)

Adult Seating: £26.00 – £37.00
Child/Senior Citizen Seating: £15.00 – £22.00
Under-18s Seating: £15.00
Note: Prices vary depending on the category of the game and the area of the ground
Programme Price: £3.00

DISABLED INFORMATION

Wheelchairs: 170 spaces in total for home and away fans in the disabled areas in the West and South Stands
Helpers: One helper admitted per disabled person
Prices: Disabled and helpers pay half normal prices
Disabled Toilets: Available in the West and South Stands
Contact: 0844 499-1234 (Bookings are necessary)
E-mail contact: disability@mfc.co.uk

Travelling Supporters' Information:
Routes: From the North: Take the A19 across the flyover and join the A66 (Eastbound). At the end of the flyover, turn left at North Ormesby where the ground is well-signposted. The ground is 200 metres down the road; From the South: Take the A1 and A19 to the junction with the A66 (Eastbound). After the flyover, turn left at North Ormesby following signs for the ground.

MILLWALL FC

Founded: 1885 (**Entered League**: 1920)
Former Names: Millwall Rovers FC (1885-1893); Millwall Athletic FC (1893-1925)
Nickname: 'Lions'
Ground: The Den, Zampa Road, London SE16 3LN
Ground Capacity: 20,146 (All seats)
Record Attendance: 20,093 (10th January 1994)

Pitch Size: 115 × 74 yards
Colours: Blue shirts with White shorts
Telephone Nº: (020) 7232-1222
Ticket Office: (020) 7231-9999
Fax Number: (020) 7231-3663
Web Site: www.millwallfc.co.uk

GENERAL INFORMATION

Car Parking: Street parking
Coach Parking: Adjacent to the ground
Nearest Railway Station: New Cross Gate (1 mile) or South Bermondsey (½ mile)
Nearest Tube: New Cross Gate (1 mile)/Canada Water (1 mile)
Club Shop: Next to the Stadium
Opening Times: Daily 9.30am to 4.30pm
Telephone Nº: (020) 7231-9845
Police Telephone Nº: (020) 7679-9217

GROUND INFORMATION

Away Supporters' Entrances & Sections:
North Stand turnstiles 31-36. A walkway from South Bermondsey Station to the ground is open on matchdays

ADMISSION INFO (2008/2009 PRICES)

Adult Seating: £20.00 – £25.00
Under-16s Seating: £10.00 – £14.00
Under-12s Seating: £7.00 – £12.00
Concessionary Seating: £13.00 – £17.00
Note: Discounts are available for members' advance purchases
Programme Price: £3.00

DISABLED INFORMATION

Wheelchairs: 78 spaces in the disabled section in the West Stand and 17 spaces for away fans in front of the North Stand
Helpers: One helper admitted per wheelchair disabled
Prices: Standard prices for the disabled. Free for helpers
Disabled Toilets: 17 toilets available around the Stadium
Commentaries are available for the blind
Contact: (020) 7232-1222 (Bookings are necessary)

Travelling Supporters' Information:
Routes: From the North: Follow City signs from the M1/A1 then signs for Shoreditch & Whitechapel. Follow Ring Road signs for Dover, cross over Tower Bridge and after 1 mile take 1st exit at the roundabout onto the A2. From Elephant and Castle take the A2 (New Kent Road) into Old Kent Road and turn left after 4 miles at Canterbury Arms pub into Ilderton Road to Zampa Road; From the South: Take the A20 & A21 following signs to London. At New Cross follow signs for Surrey Quays into Kender Street, turn left into Old Kent Road then right into Ilderton Road. Zampa Road is the 7th turning on the right; From the East: Take the A2 to New Cross (then as from the South); From the West: From M4 & M3 follow the South Circular (A205) then follow signs for Clapham, the City (A3) then Camberwell to New Cross and then as from South.

MILTON KEYNES DONS FC

Founded: 2005
Former Names: None
Nickname: 'Dons'
Ground: *stadium*mk, Stadium Way West, Milton Keynes MK1 1ST
Ground Capacity: 22,000 at present (All seats)
Pitch Size: 110 × 74 yards

Colours: White with Black and Gold trim
Telephone Nº: (01908) 622922
Ticket Office: (01908) 622900
Fax Number: (01908) 622933
Web Site: www.mkdons.com

GENERAL INFORMATION

Car Parking: 2,000 Pay and Display spaces at the Stadium
Coach Parking: By Police direction
Nearest Railway Station: Bletchley (1 mile)
Nearest Bus Station: Bletchley
Club Shop: At the Stadium
Opening Times: Weekdays 10.00amto 5.00pm with extended hours on Matchdays
Telephone Nº: (01908) 622922
Police Telephone Nº: (01908) 686001

GROUND INFORMATION

Away Supporters' Entrances & Sections:
North Stand corner, Gate 3

ADMISSION INFO (2009/2010 PRICES)

Adult Seating: £6.00 – £45.00
Child/Senior Citizen Seating: £6.00 – £35.00
Junior Seating: £1.00 – £30.00
Note: Prices vary depending on the category of the game and the area of the ground.
Programme Price: £2.50

DISABLED INFORMATION

Wheelchairs: Accommodated around the ground at concourse level
Helpers: One helper admitted per disabled person
Prices: Concessionary prices for the disabled. Helpers are admitted free of charge
Disabled Toilets: Available
Contact: (01908) 622900 (Bookings are necessary)

Travelling Supporters' Information:
Routes: From all parts: Exit the M1 at Junction 14, following signs for Milton Keynes and cross the first roundabout onto H6 Childs Way. Turn left at the next roundabout onto V11 Tongwell Street. Continue along this road then turn right at the third roundabout onto H9 Groveway. Continue along Groveway then take the first exit at the fourth roundabout towards Central Bletchley. Stadium:MK is the first turning on the left.

MORECAMBE FC

Founded: 1920 (**Entered League**: 2007)
Former Names: None
Nickname: 'Shrimps'
Ground: Christie Park, Lancaster Road, Morecambe, LA4 5TJ
Record Attendance: 9,324 (1962)
Pitch Size: 118 × 76 yards

Colours: Red shirts with White shorts
Telephone N°: (01524) 411797
Daytime Phone N°: (01524) 411797
Fax Number: (01524) 832230
Ground Capacity: 6,300
Seating Capacity: 1,200
Web site: www.morecambefc.com

GENERAL INFORMATION

Supporters Club: c/o Club
Telephone N°: –
Car Parking: At the ground
Coach Parking: At the ground
Nearest Railway Station: Morecambe Central (½ mile)
Nearest Bus Station: Morecambe
Club Shop: At the ground
Opening Times: Weekdays & Matchdays 9.00am to 5.00pm
Telephone N°: (01524) 411797
Police Telephone N°: (01524) 411534

GROUND INFORMATION

Away Supporters' Entrances & Sections:
Entrances at the corner of the South Terrace and Lancaster Road for South Terrace accommodation (when segregated)

ADMISSION INFO (2009/2010 PRICES)

Adult Standing: £13.00
Adult Seating: £15.00
Child Standing: £4.00
Child Seating: £6.00
Senior Citizen Standing: £10.00
Senior Citizen Seating: £12.00
Programme Price: £3.00

DISABLED INFORMATION

Wheelchairs: 18 spaces available in the Disabled Stand, 20 spaces in the North Stand and 10 spaces in the South Stand.
Helpers: Admitted free of charge
Prices: Concessionary prices are charged
Disabled Toilets: Available in the North and South Stands
Contact: (01524) 411797 (Bookings are preferred)

Travelling Supporters' Information:
Routes: Exit the M6 at Junction 34. Then take the A683 west in Lancaster and pick up the A589 to Morecambe. At the 2nd roundabout on the outskirts of Morecambe, take the 2nd exit into Lancaster Road and the ground is on the left, approximately 800 yards.

NEWCASTLE UNITED FC

Founded: 1882 (**Entered League:** 1893)
Former Names: Newcastle East End FC (1882-1892) amalgamated with Newcastle West End FC
Nickname: 'Magpies'
Ground: St.James' Park, Newcastle-Upon-Tyne, NE1 4ST
Ground Capacity: 52,198 (All seats)
Record Attendance: 68,386 (3rd September 1930)
Pitch Size: 115 × 74 yards
Colours: Black and White striped shirts, Black shorts
Telephone Nº: 0844 372-1892
Ticket Office: 0844 372-1892
Web Site: www.nufc.co.uk

GENERAL INFORMATION

Car Parking: Street parking
Coach Parking: By Police direction
Nearest Railway Station: Newcastle Central (¼ mile)
Nearest Bus Station: St.James' Boulevard (¼ mile)
Club Shop: At Ground, Eldon Way, MetroCentre & Monument
Opening Times: All shops are open Monday to Saturday 9.00am – 5.00pm; Eldon open until 8.00pm on Thursdays; MetroCentre open until at least 7.00pm Monday to Saturday; Monument Mall open to 8pm Thursdays & 6pm Saturdays
Telephone Nº: 0844 372-1892

GROUND INFORMATION

Away Supporters' Entrances & Sections:
Rear of the Sir John Hall Stand, entrance from Barrack Road

ADMISSION INFO (2009/2010 PRICES)

Adult Seating: £20.00 – £45.00
Child Seating: £10.00 – £23.00
Senior Citizen Seating: £15.00 – £34.00
Programme Price: £3.00

DISABLED INFORMATION

Wheelchairs: 103 spaces in total in the disabled areas throughout the stadium
Helpers: One helper admitted per disabled person
Prices: Prices available on application
Disabled Toilets: Available throughout the stadium
Commentaries are available for 20 blind supporters
Contact: Please contact the Ticket Office for information

Travelling Supporters' Information:
Routes: From the North: Follow the A1 into Newcastle, then follow Hexham signs into Percy Street. Turn right into Leazes Park Road; From the South: Take the A1M, then after Birtley Granada Services take the A1 Gateshead Western Bypass (bear left on the Motorway). Follow Airport signs for approximately 3 miles then take the A692 (Newcastle) sign, crossing the Redheugh Bridge. Proceed over three sets of traffic lights to the roundabout and take the 1st exit into Barrack Road; From the West: Take the A69 towards the City Centre. Pass Newcastle General Hospital. At the traffic lights after the Hospital turn left into Brighton Grove. After 70 yards turn right into Stanhope Street and proceed into Barrack Road for the ground.

NORTHAMPTON TOWN FC

Founded: 1897 (**Entered League:** 1920)
Nickname: 'Cobblers'
Ground: Sixfields Stadium, Upton Way, Northampton NN5 5QA
Ground Capacity: 7,653 (All seats)
Record Attendance: 7,557 (26th September 1998)
Pitch Size: 116 × 72 yards

Colours: Claret and White shirts with White shorts
Telephone Nº: (01604) 757773
Ticket Office: (01604) 588338
Fax Number: (01604) 751613
Web Site: www.ntfc.co.uk

GENERAL INFORMATION

Car Parking: At the ground
Coach Parking: At the ground
Nearest Railway Station: Northampton Castle (2 miles)
Nearest Bus Station: Greyfriars
Club Shop: At the ground
Opening Times: Monday to Thursday 10.00am – 5.00pm, Friday 10.00am – 7.00pm, non-match Saturdays 10.00am – 12.00pm and Matchdays 10.00am to kick-off and 30 minutes after the final whistle
Telephone Nº: (01604) 757773
Police Telephone Nº: (01604) 700700

GROUND INFORMATION

Away Supporters' Entrances & Sections:
Paul Cox Panel & Paint Stand

ADMISSION INFO (2009/2010 PRICES)

Adult Seating: £18.00 – £19.00
Senior Citizen Seating: £13.00 – £15.00
Under-21s Seating: £13.00 – £15.00 (Members only)
Under-16s Seating: £15.00 – £16.00
Under-7s: Admitted free of charge
Note: A range of concessionary prices are available
Programme Price: £2.00

DISABLED INFORMATION

Wheelchairs: 80 spaces in total for Home and Away fans in various areas of the ground
Helpers: One helper admitted per disabled person
Prices: £10.00 – £16.00. Contact the club for further details
Disabled Toilets: Available by the disabled areas
Commentaries are available for the blind
Contact: (01604) 588338 (Bookings are necessary)

Travelling Supporters' Information:
Routes: From All Parts: Exit the M1 at Junction 15A following the signs for Sixfields Leisure onto Upton Way – the ground is approximately 2 miles.

NORWICH CITY FC

Founded: 1902 (Entered League: 1920)
Nickname: 'Canaries'
Ground: Carrow Road, Norwich NR1 1JE
Ground Capacity: 26,034 (All seats)
Record Attendance: 43,984 (30th March 1963)
Pitch Size: 114 × 74 yards

Colours: Yellow shirts with Green shorts
Telephone Nº: (01603) 760760
Ticket Office: 0844 826-1902
Fax Number: (01603) 613886
Web Site: www.canaries.co.uk

GENERAL INFORMATION

Car Parking: City Centre car parks (nearby)
Coach Parking: Lower Clarence Road
Nearest Railway Station: Norwich Thorpe (1 mile)
Nearest Bus Station: Surrey Street, Norwich
Club Shop: In the Geoffrey Watling City Stand
Opening Times: Weekdays & Matchdays 9.00am to 5.00pm
Telephone Nº: (01603) 760760
Police Telephone Nº: (01603) 768769

GROUND INFORMATION

Away Supporters' Entrances & Sections:
Jarrold Stand usings turnstiles 51-57

ADMISSION INFO (2009/2010 PRICES)

Adult Seating: £12.00 – £35.00
Concessions & Under-16s Seating: £1.00 – £23.00
Under-12s Seating: £1.00 – £10.00
Programme Price: £3.00
Note: Prices vary according to category of game, the area of the ground and discounts which may be available

DISABLED INFORMATION

Wheelchairs: 74 spaces for home fans and 15 for away fans in Jarrold/Aviva Community Stand. Plenty of spaces are also available for ambulant disabled fans
Helpers: One helper admitted per disabled person
Prices: A single concessionary price is charged for each disabled fan and helper
Disabled Toilets: Available within the disabled area
Contact: 0844 826-1902 (Bookings are necessary)

Travelling Supporters' Information:
Routes: From the South: Take the A11 or A140 and turn right onto the A47 towards Great Yarmouth & Lowestoft, take the A146 Norwich/Lowestoft sliproad, turn left towards Norwich and follow road signs for the Football Ground; From the West: Take the A47 on to the A146 Norwich/Lowestoft slip road. Turn left towards Norwich, follow the road signs for the Football Ground.

NOTTINGHAM FOREST FC

Founded: 1865 (**Entered League**: 1892)
Nickname: 'The Reds'
Ground: The City Ground, Nottingham NG2 5FJ
Ground Capacity: 30,602 (All seats)
Record Attendance: 49,946 (28th October 1967)
Pitch Size: 112 × 78 yards

Colours: Red shirts with White shorts
Telephone Nº: (0115) 982-4444
Ticket Office: 0871 226-1980
Fax Number: (0115) 982-4455
Web Site: www.nottinghamforest.co.uk

GENERAL INFORMATION

Car Parking: East car park (limited) and street parking
Coach Parking: East car park, Meadow Lane
Nearest Railway Station: Nottingham Midland (½ mile)
Nearest Bus Station: Victoria Street/Broadmarsh Centre
Club Shop: At the ground
Opening Times: Weekdays 9.00am – 5.00pm; Matchdays 9.00am – kick-off and 30 minutes after the game; Sunday matchdays 10.00am – kick-off + 30 minutes after the game
Telephone Nº: (0115) 982-4499
Police Telephone Nº: (0115) 967-0999

GROUND INFORMATION

Away Supporters' Entrances & Sections:
Entrances via East car park for Bridgford Stand

ADMISSION INFO (2008/2009 PRICES)

Adult Seating: £20.00 – £30.00
Under-18s: £12.00
Under-12s: £6.00
Concessionary Seating: £15.00 – £22.00
Note: Discounts are available for tickets purchased in advance
Programme Price: £3.00

DISABLED INFORMATION

Wheelchairs: 12 spaces in the Brian Clough Stand, up to 22 spaces in the Lower Bridgford Stand, 15 spaces in the Upper Bridgford Stand and 13 spaces in Trent End "Castle Suite".
Helpers: One helper admitted per disabled person
Prices: Prices vary depending on the fixture. Please contact the club for further information
Disabled Toilets: Available in the Executive Stand
Contact: (0115) 982-4341 (Bookings are necessary)

Travelling Supporters' Information:
Routes: From the North: Exit the M1 at Junction 26 following Nottingham signs (A610) then signs to Melton Mowbray and Trent Bridge (A606). Cross the River Trent, turn left into Radcliffe Road then left again into Colwick Road for the ground; From the South: Exit the M1 at Junction 24 following signs for Nottingham (South) to Trent Bridge. Turn right into Radcliffe Road then left into Colwick Road; From the East: Take the A52 to West Bridgford and follow signs for Football & Cricket; From the West: Take the A52 into Nottingham, follow signs for Melton Mowbray and Trent Bridge, cross the River Trent (then as North).

NOTTS COUNTY FC

Founded: 1862 (**Entered League:** 1888)
Nickname: 'Magpies'
Ground: Meadow Lane, Nottingham NG2 3HJ
Ground Capacity: 20,300 (All seats)
Record Attendance: 47,310 (12th March 1955)
Pitch Size: 113 × 70 yards

Colours: Black and White striped shirts, Black shorts
Telephone Nº: (0115) 952-9000
Ticket Office: (0115) 955-7204 (weekdays), (0115) 955-7210 (matchdays)
Fax Number: (0115) 955-3994
Web Site: www.nottscountyfc.co.uk

GENERAL INFORMATION

Car Parking: British Waterways, Meadow Lane
Coach Parking: Incinerator Road (Cattle Market Corner)
Nearest Railway Station: Nottingham Midland (½ mile)
Nearest Bus Station: Broadmarsh Centre
Club Shop: At the ground
Opening Times: Closed Mondays; Tuesday to Friday 9.00am – 5.00pm, Saturday Matchdays 9.30am – 5.30pm, other Saturdays 9.00am – 1.00pm
Telephone Nº: (0115) 952-9000
Police Telephone Nº: (0115) 948-1888

GROUND INFORMATION

Away Supporters' Entrances & Sections:
Jimmy Sirrel Stand, Block X – use Turnstiles 27-31

ADMISSION INFO (2009/2010 PRICES)

Adult Seating: £18.00 – £20.00
Child Seating: £5.00 (Under-16s)
Concessionary Seating: £12.00
Programme Price: £2.50

DISABLED INFORMATION

Wheelchairs: 100 spaces in total in the disabled area, County Road/Meadow Lane End corner
Helpers: One helper admitted per disabled fan
Prices: 25% reduction from normal prices for the disabled. Helpers are admitted free of charge
Disabled Toilets: Available next to the disabled area
Contact: (0115) 955-7204 (Bookings are necessary)

Travelling Supporters' Information:
Routes: From the North: Exit the M1 at Junction 26 following Nottingham signs (A610) then Melton Mowbray and Trent Bridge (A606) signs. Before the River Trent turn left into Meadow Lane; From the South: Exit the M1 at Junction 24 following signs for Nottingham (South) to Trent Bridge, cross the river and follow the one-way system to the right, then turn left and right at the traffic lights then second right into Meadow Lane; From the East: Take the A52 to West Bridgford/Trent Bridge, cross the river and follow the one-way system to the right then turn left and right at the traffic lights, then second right into Meadow Lane; From the West: Take the A52 into Nottingham following signs for Melton Mowbray and Trent Bridge. Before the River Trent turn left into Meadow Lane.

OLDHAM ATHLETIC FC

Founded: 1895 (**Entered League**: 1907)
Former Names: Pine Villa FC (1895-1899)
Nickname: 'Latics'
Ground: Boundary Park, Oldham OL1 2PA
Ground Capacity: 10,904 (All seats)
Record Attendance: 47,671 (25th January 1930)
Pitch Size: 110 × 72 yards

Colours: Royal Blue shirts and shorts, White socks
Telephone Nº: 0871 226-2235
Ticket Office: 0871 226-1653
Fax Number: 0871 226-1715
Web Site: www.oldhamathletic.co.uk

GENERAL INFORMATION

Car Parking: Broadway Stand car park (1,000 cars)
Coach Parking: At the ground
Nearest Railway Station: Oldham Werneth (1½ miles)
Nearest Bus Station: Oldham Town Centre (2 miles)
Club Shop: At the ground
Opening Times: Mondays to Fridays 9.00am to 5.00pm. Saturdays 9.00am to 12.00pm
Telephone Nº: 0871 226-1679
Police Telephone Nº: (0161) 624-0444

GROUND INFORMATION

Away Supporters' Entrances & Sections:
Rochdale Road Stand

ADMISSION INFO (2009/2010 PRICES)

Adult Seating: £16.00 – £20.00
Senior Citizen/Under-16s Seating: £10.00 – £11.00
Under-12s Seating: £3.00
Note: Discounts are available for tickets purchased in advance
Programme Price: £3.00

DISABLED INFORMATION

Wheelchairs: 60 spaces in the disabled areas – Broadway Paddock, Chadderton Road Stand and Rochdale Road Stand
Helpers: One helper admitted per disabled person
Prices: Normal prices for the disabled. Free for helpers
Disabled Toilets: Available in Broadway Paddock and the Rochdale Road Stand
Contact: 0871 226-2235 (Bookings are necessary)

Travelling Supporters' Information:
Routes: From All Parts: Exit the M62 at Junction 20 and take the A627M to the junction with the A664. Take the 1st exit at the roundabout onto Broadway, then the 1st right into Hilbre Avenue which leads to the car park at the ground.

PETERBOROUGH UNITED FC

Founded: 1934 (Entered League: 1960)
Nickname: 'Posh'
Ground: London Road, Peterborough PE2 8AL
Ground Capacity: 14,584
Seating Capacity: 8,422
Record Attendance: 30,096 (20th February 1965)
Pitch Size: 112 × 71 yards

Colours: Cobalt Blue & White shirts and shorts
Telephone Nº: (01733) 563947
Ticket Office: (01733) 865674
Fax Number: (01733) 344140
Web Site: www.theposh.com

GENERAL INFORMATION

Car Parking: At the ground and also adjacent
Coach Parking: In front of the (North) Main Stand
Nearest Railway Station: Peterborough (1 mile)
Nearest Bus Station: Peterborough (1 mile)
Club Shop: At the ground
Opening Times: Monday to Thursday 9.00am to 5.00pm, Fridays 10.00am to 5.00pm and Saturday Matchdays 10.00pm to 3.00pm then 5.00pm to 5.30pm
Telephone Nº: (01733) 563947
Police Telephone Nº: (01733) 563232

GROUND INFORMATION

Away Supporters' Entrances & Sections:
A North Block (Seating) and Moyes End (Terrace)

ADMISSION INFO (2009/2010 PRICES)

Adult Standing: £17.00
Adult Seating: £22.00
Senior Citizen Standing/Seating: £14.00
Student Standing/Seating: £14.00
Under-16s Standing: £10.00
Under-16s Seating: £5.00 in the Family Stand, £10.00 in the North Stand
Note: Under-10s are admitted free in the South Stand
Programme Price: £3.00

DISABLED INFORMATION

Wheelchairs: 26 spaces in total for Home and Away fans in disabled area, right side of South Stand
Helpers: One helper admitted per disabled person
Prices: £14.00 for the disabled. Free of charge for helpers
Disabled Toilets: Available in the South and Main Stands
Contact: (01733) 563947 (Bookings are necessary)

Travelling Supporters' Information:
Routes: From the North and West: Take the A1 then the A47 into the Town Centre and follow Whittlesey signs across the river into London Road; From the East: Take the A47 into the Town Centre (then as from the North); From the South: Take the A1 then the A15 into London Road.

PLYMOUTH ARGYLE FC

Founded: 1886 **(Entered League:** 1920)
Former Names: Argyle FC (1886-1903)
Nickname: 'Pilgrims' 'Argyle'
Ground: Home Park, Plymouth PL2 3DQ
Ground Capacity: 19,810 (All seats)
Record Attendance: 43,596 (10th October 1936)

Pitch Size: 112 × 72 yards
Colours: Green shirts and White shorts
Telephone N°: (01752) 562561
Box Office: 0845 338-7232
Fax Number: (01752) 606167
Web Site: www.pafc.co.uk

GENERAL INFORMATION

Car Parking: Car park for 1,000 cars is adjacent
Coach Parking: Central Park Car Park
Nearest Railway Station: Plymouth North Road
Nearest Bus Station: Bretonside, Plymouth
Club Shop: At the ground and Drake Circus Shopping Mall
Opening Times: Ground shop: Monday to Friday 9.00am – 5.00pm, Non-match Saturdays 9.00am – 3.00pm, Saturday Matchdays 9.00am – 3.00pm + 30 minutes after the game. Drake Circus shop: Monday to Saturday 9.00am to 6.00pm (8.00pm on Thursdays). Also Sundays 10.30am – 4.30pm
Telephone N°: (01752) 562561
Police Telephone N°: 0990 777444

GROUND INFORMATION

Away Supporters' Entrances & Sections:
Barn Park End turnstiles for covered accommodation

ADMISSION INFO (2009/2010 PRICES)

Adult Seating: £19.00 – £26.00
Under-18s Seating: £6.00 – £8.00
Senior Citizen/Under-23s Seating: £13.00 – £18.00
Note: Discounted prices are available if tickets are bought before 5.00pm on the day prior to the game
Programme Price: £3.00

DISABLED INFORMATION

Wheelchairs: 60 spaces Home fans and 25 spaces for Away fans in the disabled sections
Helpers: One helper admitted per disabled person
Prices: Normal prices for the disabled. Free for helpers
Disabled Toilets: Available throughout the stadium
Commentaries are available for the visually impaired
Contact: (01752) 562561 (Barry Hardman – Bookings are necessary)

Travelling Supporters' Information:
Routes: From All Parts: Take the A38 to Tavistock Road (A386), then branch left following signs for Home Park (A386) and continue for 1¼ miles. The car park for the ground is on the left (signposted Home Park).

PORTSMOUTH FC

Founded: 1898 (**Entered League**: 1920)
Nickname: 'Pompey'
Ground: Fratton Park, 57 Frogmore Road, Portsmouth, Hants PO4 8RA
Ground Capacity: 20,200 (All seats)
Record Attendance: 51,385 (26th February 1949)
Pitch Size: 108 × 71 yards

Colours: Blue shirts and shorts
Telephone Nº: (023) 9273-1204
Ticket Office: 08442 777879
Fax Number: (023) 9273-4129
Web Site: www.portsmouthfc.co.uk

GENERAL INFORMATION

Car Parking: Street parking
Coach Parking: By Police direction
Nearest Railway Station: Fratton (adjacent)
Nearest Bus Station: –
Club Shop: At the ground (Rodney Road)
Opening Times: Monday to Friday 9.00am – 5.30pm and Saturdays 9.00am – 4.00pm. Matchday Saturdays shuts between 3.00pm–4.45pm
Telephone Nº: (023) 9273-8358
Police Telephone Nº: (023) 9232-1111

GROUND INFORMATION

Away Supporters' Entrances & Sections:
Aspley Road – Milton Road side for Aspley Road End

ADMISSION INFO (2009/2010 PRICES)

Adult Seating: £34.00 – £42.00
Child Seating: £10.00 – £22.00
Senior Citizen Seating: £20.00 – £30.00
Note: Prices vary depending on the category of the game
Programme Price: £3.00

DISABLED INFORMATION

Wheelchairs: Limited number of spaces available in the disabled section, Fratton End
Helpers: One helper admitted per disabled person
Prices: £15.00 for the disabled. Free of charge for helpers
Disabled Toilets: One available in disabled section
Contact: (023) 9273-1204 (Bookings are necessary)

Travelling Supporters' Information:
Routes: From the North and West: Take the M27 and M275 to the end then take the 2nd exit at the roundabout and after ¼ mile turn right at the 'T' junction into London Road (A2047). After 1¼ miles cross the railway bridge and turn left into Goldsmith Avenue. After ½ mile turn left into Frogmore Road; From the East: Take the A27 following Southsea signs (A2030). Turn left at the roundabout (3 miles) onto the A288, then right into Priory Crescent and next right into Carisbrooke Road for the ground.

PORT VALE FC

Founded: 1876 (**Entered League**: 1892)
Former Names: Burslem Port Vale FC
Nickname: 'Valiants'
Ground: Vale Park, Hamil Road, Burslem, Stoke-on-Trent ST6 1AW
Ground Capacity: 19,148 (All seats)
Record Attendance: 49,768 (20nd February 1960)
Pitch Size: 114 × 78 yards

Colours: Black and White striped shirts with a White back, Black shorts
Telephone Nº: (01782) 655800
Ticket Office: (01782) 655832
Fax Number: (01782) 834981
Web Site: www.port-vale.co.uk

GENERAL INFORMATION

Car Parking: Car parks at the ground
Coach Parking: Hamil Road car park
Nearest Railway Station: Stoke
Nearest Bus Station: Burslem (adjacent)
Club Shop: At the ground
Opening Times: Monday to Saturday 9.00am – 5.00pm
Telephone Nº: (01782) 655833

GROUND INFORMATION

Away Supporters' Entrances & Sections:
Hamil Road turnstiles, numbers 1 to 8

ADMISSION INFO (2009/2010 PRICES)

Adult Seating: £19.00
Child Seating: £8.00 (Under-9s admitted free of charge)
Senior Citizen Seating: £12.50
Programme Price: £2.50

DISABLED INFORMATION

Wheelchairs: 46 spaces available in the Disabled Stand, Lorne Street/Bycars Corner
Helpers: One helper admitted per disabled person
Prices: Normal prices for disabled fans. Free for helpers
Disabled Toilets: Available in the disabled area
Commentaries are available – please contact the club
Contact: (01782) 655800 (Bookings are necessary)

Travelling Supporters' Information:
Routes: From the North: Exit the M6 at Junction 16 and follow Stoke signs (A500). Branch left off the A500 at the exit signposted Tunstall and take the 2nd exit at the roundabout into Newcastle Street. Proceed through the traffic lights into Moorland Road and take the 2nd turning on the left into Hamil Road; From the South and West: Exit the M6 at Junction 15 and take the A5006 and A500. After 6¼ miles branch left (then as from the North); From the East: Take the A50 or A52 into Stoke following Burslem signs into Waterloo Road, turn right at Burslem crossroads into Moorland Road (then as from the North).

PRESTON NORTH END FC

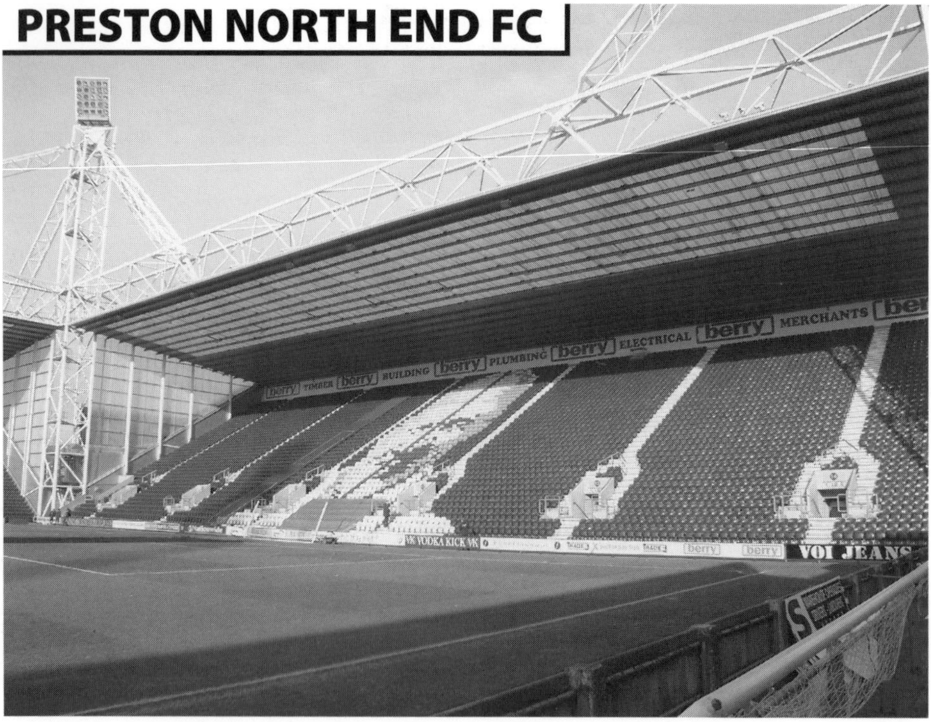

Founded: 1881 (**Entered League**: 1888)
Nickname: 'Lilywhites' 'North End'
Ground: Deepdale, Preston PR1 6RU
Ground Capacity: 23,408 (All seats)
Record Attendance: 42,684 (23rd April 1938)
Pitch Size: 110 × 72 yards

Colours: White shirts with Blue shorts
Telephone Nº: 0844 856-1964
Ticket Office: 0844 856-1966
Fax Number: (01772) 693366
Web Site: www.pne.com

GENERAL INFORMATION

Car Parking: Four official car parks at the stadium plus further parking at Moor Park and Deepdale Primary School
Coach Parking: Deepdale Retail Park
Nearest Railway Station: Preston (2 miles)
Nearest Bus Station: Preston (1 mile)
Club Shop: At the ground
Opening Times: Monday to Saturday 9.00am to 5.00pm, Sunday 11.00am to 4.00pm
Telephone Nº: 0844 856-1964
Police Telephone Nº: (01772) 203203

GROUND INFORMATION

Away Supporters' Entrances & Sections:
Bill Shankly Kop

ADMISSION INFO (2009/2010 PRICES)

Adult Seating: £20.00 – £27.00
Child Seating: £5.00 (Under-8s admitted free)
Senior Citizen Seating: £12.00 – £20.00
Family Tickets: From £25.00 (1 adult + 2 children)
Programme Price: £3.50

DISABLED INFORMATION

Wheelchairs: Spaces available for advance order
Helpers: One helper admitted per wheelchair
Prices: £20.00 – £22.00 for the disabled. Free for helpers
Disabled Toilets: Available throughout the ground
Commentaries are available for the blind
Contact: 0844 856-1964 (Bookings are usually necessary)

Travelling Supporters' Information:
Routes: From the North: Take the M6 then the M55 to Junction 1. Follow signs for Preston (A6). After 2 miles turn left at the crossroads into Blackpool Road (A5085). Turn right ¾ mile into Deepdale; From the South and East: Exit the M6 at Junction 31 and follow Preston signs (A59). Take the 2nd exit at the roundabout (1 mile) into Blackpool Road. Turn left after 1¼ miles into Deepdale; From the West: Exit the M55 at Junction 1 (then as from the North).

QUEEN'S PARK RANGERS FC

Founded: 1882 (**Entered League:** 1920)
Former Names: Formed by the amalgamation of St. Jude's FC and Christchurch Rangers FC
Nickname: 'Rangers' 'R's'
Ground: Loftus Road Stadium, South Africa Road, London W12 7PJ
Ground Capacity: 18,309 (All seats)
Record Attendance: 35,353 (27th April 1974)

Pitch Size: 112 × 72 yards
Colours: Blue and White hooped shirts, White shorts
Telephone Nº: (020) 8743-0262
Ticket Office: 08444 777007
Fax Number: (020) 8749-0994
Web Site: www.qpr.co.uk

GENERAL INFORMATION

Car Parking: Street parking
Coach Parking: By Police direction
Nearest Railway Station: Ealing Broadway
Nearest Tube Station: White City (Central)
Club Shop: At the ground
Opening Times: Monday to Saturday 9.00am – 5.00pm and Sundays 10.00am – 4.00pm
Telephone Nº: (020) 8749-6862
Police Telephone Nº: (020) 8741-6212

GROUND INFORMATION

Away Supporters' Entrances & Sections:
South Africa Road turnstiles 13-15 & Ellerslie Road turnstiles 9-12 for School End Stand

ADMISSION INFO (2009/2010 PRICES)

Adult Seating: £20.00 – £35.00
Child Seating: £12.00 – £25.00 (Under-8s admitted free)
Senior Citizen/Ages 16-21 Seating: £12.00 – £25.00
Programme Price: £3.00

DISABLED INFORMATION

Wheelchairs: 25 spaces available in the disabled section
Helpers: One helper admitted per wheelchair
Prices: Concessionary prices for disabled. Free for helpers
Disabled Toilets: Available
Commentaries for the blind are available in the Ellerslie Road Stand
Contact: (020) 8740-2504 (Bookings are necessary)

Travelling Supporters' Information:
Routes: From the North: Take M1 & M406 North Circular for Neasden, go left after ¾ mile (A404) following signs for Harlesden, Hammersmith, past White City Stadium, right into White City Road and left into South Africa Road; From the South: Take A206 then A3 across Putney Bridge and follow signs to Hammersmith then Oxford (A219) to Shepherd's Bush. Join the A4020 following signs to Acton, turn right (¼ mile) into Loftus Road; From the East: Take the A12, A406 then the A503 to join the Ring Road, follow Oxford signs and join the A40(M), branch left (2 miles) to the M41, take the 3rd exit at the roundabout to the A4020 (then as South); From the West: Take the M4 to Chiswick then the A315 & A402 to Shepherd's Bush, join A4020 (then as South).

READING FC

Founded: 1871 (**Entered League**: 1920)
Former Names: Formed by the amalgamation of Hornets FC (1877) and Earley FC (1889)
Nickname: 'Royals'
Ground: Madejski Stadium, Junction 11 M4, Reading, Berkshire RG2 0FL
Ground Capacity: 24,200 (All seats)
Record Attendance: 24,107 (3rd December 2004)
Pitch Size: 111 × 74 yards
Colours: Blue and White hooped shirts, White shorts
Telephone Nº: (0118) 968-1100
Ticket Office: 0844 279-1871
Fax Number: (0118) 968-1101
Web Site: www.readingfc.co.uk

GENERAL INFORMATION

Car Parking: 1,800 spaces available at the ground. Also another 2,000 spaces available nearby
Coach Parking: By Police direction (at the ground)
Nearest Railway Station: Reading Central
Nearest Bus Station: Reading
Club Shop: At the ground
Opening Times: Monday to Saturday 9.00am – 5.30pm, Sundays 10.00am – 4.00pm
Telephone Nº: (0118) 968-1234
Police Telephone Nº: (0118) 953-6000

GROUND INFORMATION

Away Supporters' Entrances & Sections: South Stand entrances and accommodation

ADMISSION INFO (2009/2010 PRICES)

Adult Seating: £22.50 – £25.50
Concessionary Seating: £16.50 – £17.50
Child Seating: £11.50 – £12.50
Note: Prices shown are for tickets purchased in advance. Matchday prices are £4.00 more expensive
Programme Price: £3.00

DISABLED INFORMATION

Wheelchairs: A total of 128 spaces available for wheelchairs throughout the stadium
Helpers: Yes
Prices: £22.50–£25.50 for each disabled fan and one helper.
Disabled Toilets: One available adjacent to stand
Commentaries for approximately 12 people are available
Contact: 0844 279-1871 (Bookings are necessary)

Travelling Supporters' Information:
Routes: The stadium is situated just off Junction 11 of the M4 near Reading.

ROCHDALE FC

Founded: 1907 (**Entered League**: 1921)
Former Names: Rochdale Town FC
Nickname: 'The Dale'
Ground: Spotland Stadium, Rochdale OL11 5DS
Ground Capacity: 10,034
Seating Capacity: 7,913
Record Attendance: 24,231 (10th December 1949)

Pitch Size: 114 × 76 yards
Colours: Black and Blue striped shirts, White shorts
Telephone N°: (01706) 644648
Ticket Office: (01706) 644648
Fax Number: (01706) 648466
Web Site: www.rochdaleafc.co.uk

GENERAL INFORMATION

Car Parking: Street parking only
Coach Parking: By Police direction
Nearest Railway Station: Rochdale (2 miles)
Nearest Bus Station: Town Centre (1 mile)
Club Shop: At the ground
Opening Times: Weekdays and Saturday Matchdays from 9.00am to 5.00pm
Telephone N°: (01706) 644648
Police Telephone N°: (0161) 872-5050

GROUND INFORMATION

Away Supporters' Entrances & Sections:
Turnstiles 11 to 18 for Willbutts Lane

ADMISSION INFO (2009/2010 PRICES)

Adult Standing: £14.00
Adult Seating: £17.00 – £20.00
Child/Senior Citizen Standing: £9.00
Child Seating: £5.00 (Only available for accompanied Under-16s in the Family Stand – Under-7s admitted free)
Senior Citizen Seating: £10.00 – £12.00
Programme Price: £2.50

DISABLED INFORMATION

Wheelchairs: 24 spaces in total in the disabled sections in the Main, W.M.G. and Willbutts Lane Stands
Helpers: One helper admitted per disabled person
Prices: Concessionary prices for disabled. Free for helpers
Disabled Toilets: Available adjacent to disabled area
Contact: (01706) 644648 (Bookings are necessary)

Travelling Supporters' Information:
Routes: From All Parts: Exit the M62 at Junction 20 and take the A627M signposted Rochdale. At the end of this link road, filter left carry on for 400 yards and go straight on at the roundabout into Roche Valley Way signposted Spotland Stadium. At the traffic lights go staight ahead and the ground is on the right after ½ mile.

ROTHERHAM UNITED FC

Founded: 1870 (Entered League: 1893)
Former Names: Rotherham Town FC (1870-1896), Thornhill United FC (1884-1905) and Rotherham County FC (1905-1925)
Nickname: 'The Millers'
Ground: Don Valley Stadium, Worksop Road, Sheffield S9 3TL
Stadium Telephone Nº: (0114) 223-3600
Ground Capacity: 25,000 (All seats)

Pitch Size: 110 × 72 yards
Record Attendance: 25,170 (13/12/1952 – Millmoor)
Colours: Red shirts with White sleeves, White shorts
Contact Telephone Nº: 08444 140733
Ticket Office: 08444 140737
Fax Number: 08444 140744
Office Address: Mangham House, Mangham Road, Barbot Hall Industrial Estate, Rotherham S61 4RJ
Web Site: www.themillers.co.uk

GENERAL INFORMATION

Car Parking: 350 spaces at the stadium + street parking
Coach Parking: By Police direction
Nearest Railway Station: Sheffield Meadowhall (¾ mile)
Nearest Bus Station: Sheffield Meadowhall (¾ mile)
Club Shop: At the Office Address (see above) and also at the Stadium on matchdays.
Opening Times: Office Address: Weekdays 9.00am to 5.00pm (5.30pm on Mondays and 6.30pm on Wednesdays). Non-Saturday Matchdays 10.00am to 2.00pm.
Don Valley Stadium: Matchdays 1.00pm to 3.00pm
Telephone Nº: 08444 140733

GROUND INFORMATION

Away Supporters' Entrances & Sections:
Turnstiles N and M (covered seating)

ADMISSION INFO (2009/2010 PRICES)

Adult Seating: £18.00
Senior Citizen/Student Seating: £10.00
Ages 12-16 Seating: £6.00
Ages 8-11 Seating: £5.00
Programme Price: £2.50

DISABLED INFORMATION

Wheelchairs: Accommodated
Helpers: One helper admitted per disabled person
Prices: Disabled are charged £10.00 each. Helpers are admitted free of charge
Disabled Toilets: Available
Contact: 08444 140733 (Bookings are necessary)

Travelling Supporters' Information:
Routes: Exit the M1 at Junction 34 and take the A6178 into Sheffield. Continue past the A6102 (Greenland Road) junction on the left along Attercliffe Common, turn left into Leeds Road at the junction with Newhall Road and the stadium is on the left. Trains run directly to the stadium from Sheffield Meadowhall transport interchange.

SCUNTHORPE UNITED FC

Founded: 1899 (**Entered League**: 1950)
Former Name: Scunthorpe and Lindsey United FC (1899-1912)
Nickname: 'The Iron'
Ground: Glanford Park, Doncaster Road, Scunthorpe, North Lincolnshire DN15 8TD
Ground Capacity: 9,095
Seating Capacity: 6,322
Record Attendance: 8,906 (10th March 2007)
Pitch Size: 112 × 72 yards
Colours: Shirts and shorts are Claret with Sky Blue trim
Telephone N°: 0871 221-1899
Ticket Office: 0871 221-1899
Fax Number: (01724) 857986
Web Site: www.scunthorpe-united.co.uk

GENERAL INFORMATION

Car Parking: Spaces for 800 cars at the ground
Coach Parking: At the ground
Nearest Railway Station: Scunthorpe (1½ miles)
Nearest Bus Station: Scunthorpe (1½ miles)
Club Shop: At the ground
Opening Times: Weekdays 9.00am to 5.00pm
Matchdays 10.00am to 3.00pm and 4.45pm to 5.15pm
Telephone N°: (01724) 747682
Police Telephone N°: (01724) 282888

GROUND INFORMATION

Away Supporters' Entrances & Sections:
Turnstiles 6-7 for the AMS Stand

ADMISSION INFO (2009/2010 PRICES)

Adult Standing: £14.50 – £15.50
Adult Seating: £17.50 – £27.50
Concessionary Standing: £9.50 – £10.50
Concessionary Seating: £10.50 – £20.50
Under-16s Standing: £5.50 – £6.50
Under-16s Seating: £5.50 – £6.50
Programme Price: £3.00

DISABLED INFORMATION

Wheelchairs: 10 spaces for Home fans and 6 spaces for Away fans in the disabled section, Grove Wharf Stand
Helpers: One helper admitted per disabled person
Prices: Normal prices for the disabled. Free for helpers
Disabled Toilets: One available in the disabled area
Commentaries are available for the blind
Contact: 0871-221-1899 (Bookings are necessary)

Travelling Supporters' Information:
Routes: From All Parts: Exit the M180 at Junction 3 onto the M181. Follow the M181 to the roundabout with the A18 and take the A18 towards Scunthorpe – the ground is on the right after 200 yards.

SHEFFIELD UNITED FC

Founded: 1889 (**Entered League**: 1892)
Nickname: 'Blades'
Ground: Bramall Lane, Sheffield S2 4SU
Ground Capacity: 32,609 (All seats)
Record Attendance: 68,287 (15th February 1936)
Pitch Size: 110 × 73 yards

Colours: Red and White striped shirts, Black shorts
Telephone Nº: 0871 222-1899
Ticket Office: 0871 222-1899
Fax Number: 0871 663-2430
Web Site: www.sufc.co.uk

GENERAL INFORMATION

Car Parking: Street parking only
Coach Parking: By Police direction
Nearest Railway Station: Sheffield Midland (1 mile)
Nearest Bus Station: Pond Street, Sheffield (1 mile)
Club Shop: At the ground
Opening Times: Monday to Friday 9.30am – 5.30pm and Matchdays from 9.00am – 5.30pm
Telephone Nº: 0871 663-2489
Police Telephone Nº: (0114) 220-2020

GROUND INFORMATION

Away Supporters' Entrances & Sections:
Visitors' Box Office – Bramall Lane Stand Lower Tier

ADMISSION INFO (2008/2009 PRICES)

Adult Seating: £15.00 – £34.00
Child Seating: £10.00 – £12.00
Concessionary Seating: £10.00 – £24.00
Note: Prices vary according to the category of the game
Programme Price: £4.00

DISABLED INFORMATION

Wheelchairs: Limited number of spaces available in the disabled section – Members area
Helpers: One helper admitted per wheelchair
Prices: £10.00 for the disabled
Disabled Toilets: 7 available within the enclosure
Commentaries available for the blind on request
Contact: 0871 222-1889 (Bookings are necessary)

Travelling Supporters' Information:
Routes: From the North: Exit the M1 at Junction 33 following signs to Sheffield (A57) and continue along Sheffield Parkway until the Park Square roundabout. Take the 3rd exit and follow the A61 (Sheffield). Midland Station is on the left, the road veers to the left then take the middle lane following the ring road to the right. Take the first exit at the roundabout into Bramhall Lane.; From the South: Exit the M1 at junction 29 and take the A617 (Chesterfield). Take the 3rd exit at the roundabout onto the A61 and continue to the Earl of Arundel and Surrey Public House. Turn left and continue into Bramhall Lane; From the East: Exit the M1 at Junctions 31 or 33 and take the A57 to the roundabout, take the 3rd exit into Sheaf Street (then as from the North); From the West: Take the A57 into Sheffield and take the 4th exit at the roundabout into Upper Hanover Street and at the 2nd roundabout take the 3rd exit into Bramall Lane.

SHEFFIELD WEDNESDAY FC

Founded: 1867 (**Entered League**: 1892)
Former Name: The Wednesday FC
Nickname: 'Owls'
Ground: Hillsborough, Sheffield S6 1SW
Ground Capacity: 39,812 (All seats)
Record Attendance: 72,841 (17th February 1934)
Pitch Size: 110 × 71 yards

Colours: Blue and White striped shirts, Black shorts
Telephone Nº: 0870 999-1867
Ticket Office: 0870 995-1867
Fax Number: (0114) 221-2122
Web Site: www.swfc.co.uk

GENERAL INFORMATION

Car Parking: Street parking
Coach Parking: Clay Wheels Lane
Nearest Railway Station: Sheffield Midland (4 miles)
Nearest Bus Station: Pond Street, Sheffield (4 miles)
Club Shop: At the ground
Ground Opening Times: Monday to Friday from 8.45am to 5.15pm and Saturday from 9.00am to 12.00pm
Telephone Nº: 0870 999-1867
Police Telephone Nº: (0114) 220-2020

GROUND INFORMATION

Away Supporters' Entrances & Sections:
West Stand turnstiles for West Stand, Upper Tier

ADMISSION INFO (2009/2010 PRICES)

Adult Seating: £18.00 – £25.00
Concessionary Seating: £9.00 – £15.00
Note: Prices vary depending on the category of the match
Programme Price: £3.00

DISABLED INFORMATION

Wheelchairs: 257 spaces for disabled fans including 88 wheelchair spaces for home fans, and 9 wheelchair spaces for visiting fans in the disabled section – North Stand & West Stand Lower
Helpers: One helper admitted per disabled person
Prices: No charge for the disabled or helpers
Disabled Toilets: Available in the North and West Stands
Commentaries are available for the blind
Contact: 0870 999-1867 (Bookings are necessary)

Travelling Supporters' Information:
Routes: From the North, South and East: Exit the M1 at Junction 36 and follow signs to Sheffield (A61). Continue for 4 miles then take the 3rd exit at the 2nd roundabout into Leppings Lane. The ground is situated on the left; From the West: Take the A57 until the road splits in two. Take the left fork (A6101). After 3¾ miles turn left onto the one-way system and follow the road round to the right onto Holme Lane. This road becomes Bradfield Road. At the junction with the A61 (Penistone Road), turn left towards Barnsley. The stadium is on the left after Hillsborough Park.

√ OLD √

SHREWSBURY TOWN FC

Founded: 1886 (**Entered League**: 1950)
Nickname: 'Town'
Ground: The New Meadow, Oteley Road, Shrewsbury SY2 6ST
Ground Capacity: 10,000 (All seats)
Record Attendance: 18,917 (26th April 1961 at Gay Meadow)

Pitch Size: 116 × 75 yards
Colours: Shirts and shorts are Blue with Amber and White trim
Telephone Nº: (01743) 360111
Ticket Office: (01743) 360111
Fax Number: (01743) 236384
Web Site: www.shrewsburytown.com

GENERAL INFORMATION

Car Parking: Limited parking at the stadium – Permit Holders only. Parking restrictions are imposted on matchdays with no parking allowed in the vicinity of the stadium. Visiting fans should use the Park & Ride Scheme – cost £2.00 per person for the return journey – see below
Coach Parking: At the stadium
Nearest Railway Station: Shrewsbury (2½ miles)
Nearest Bus Station: Raven Meadows, Shrewsbury
Club Shop: At the ground
Opening Times: Matchdays and Office Hours
Telephone Nº: (01743) 360111
Police Telephone Nº: (01743) 232888

GROUND INFORMATION

Away Supporters' Entrances & Sections: North Stand

ADMISSION INFO (2008/2009 PRICES)

Adult Seating: £18.00 – £21.00
Child Seating: £5.00 – £15.00 (Cheaper for members)
Senior Citizen/Student Seating: £13.00 – £15.00
Note: Tickets are £2.00 cheaper if bought before the day of the match. A range of discounted Family Tickets are available – please contact the club for further details.
Programme Price: £2.50

DISABLED INFORMATION

Wheelchairs: Spaces in the North, South and East Stands
Helpers: One helper admitted per disabled person
Prices: £13.00 – £15.00 for the disabled (cheaper if bought before the matchday). Helpers are admitted free of charge
Disabled Toilets: Available throughout the ground
Contact: (01743) 360111 (Bookings are necessary)

Travelling Supporters' Information:
Park & Ride information: Buses run every 15 minutes from 12.30pm to 2.30pm on Saturday matchdays and 6.15pm to 7.30pm on matchdays in the week. Parking is free and the return bus journey is £2.00 per person. Buses return to the car parks immediately after the match finishes and car parks will remain open for one hour only. Car Park Locations:
Oxon Park and Ride Site: From the West and North West. At the junction of the A5 and the A458 (Churncote Roundabout) follow the signs A458 'Shrewsbury Town Centre'. Oxon Park and Ride Site is clearly signposted; **The Shirehall**: From all routes proceed along the A5 to Emstrey Island Roundabout into Shrewsbury, take the A5064 along London Road to the Column roundabout. Take the 3rd exit at the roundabout and the first right into the Shirehall Car Park; **Shirehall Overflow Car Park**: Follow directions to London Road as above. Before you reach the roundabout the car park is on the right-hand side. Proceed on foot to the Shirehall main car park for the bus.

SOUTHAMPTON FC

Founded: 1885 (Entered League: 1920)
Former Names: Southampton St. Mary's YMCA FC (1885-1897)
Nickname: 'Saints'
Ground: St. Mary's Stadium, Britannia Road, Southampton SO14 5FP
Ground Capacity: 32,689 (All seats)
Record Attendance: 32,151 (29th December 2003)
Pitch Size: 112 × 72 yards
Colours: Red and White shirts with Black shorts
Telephone Nº: 0845 688-9448
Ticket Office: 0800 280-0050
Ticket Office Fax Number: 0845 688-9291
General Fax Number: (023) 8072-7727
Ticket Information Nº: 0845 688-9288
Web Site: www.saintsfc.co.uk

GENERAL INFORMATION

Car Parking: Park & Ride only – must be pre-booked
Coach Parking: By Police direction
Nearest Railway Station: Southampton Central
Nearest Bus Station: Western Esplanade
Club Shop: At the ground and also at West Quay
Opening Times: Monday to Saturday 9.00am – 5.00pm
Telephone Nº: 0845 688-9433
Police Telephone Nº: (023) 8033-5444

GROUND INFORMATION

Away Supporters' Entrances & Sections:
Northam Stand

ADMISSION INFO (2009/2010 PRICES)

Adult Seating: £22.00 – £28.00
Under-16s Seating: £9.00 – £28.00
Student/Senior Citizen Seating: £16.00 – £28.00
Programme Price: £3.00

DISABLED INFORMATION

Wheelchairs: 200 spaces in total for Home and Away fans throughout the ground
Helpers: One helper admitted per disabled person
Prices: £11.00 for each disabled fan.
Disabled Toilets: Available in all Stands
Contact: (023) 8072-7777 (Bookings are necessary)
E-mail Contact: disability@saintsfc.co.uk

Travelling Supporters' Information:
Routes: Although the ground is situated in the Melbourne Street/Marine Parade area of Southampton, no parking is available in the immediate vicinity except by special arrangement for Disabled supporters. There are a number of well-signposted Park and Ride car parks around the City and those designated for Away fans should be clearly marked.

SOUTHEND UNITED FC

Founded: 1906 (**Entered League**: 1920)
Former Name: Southend Athletic FC
Nickname: 'Shrimpers' 'Blues'
Ground: Roots Hall Ground, Victoria Avenue, Southend-on-Sea SS2 6NQ
Ground Capacity: 12,163 (All seats)
Record Attendance: 31,033 (10th January 1979)

Pitch Size: 110 × 74 yards
Colours: Shirts and shorts are Blue
Telephone No: (01702) 304050
Ticket Office: 08444 770077
Fax Number: (01702) 304124
Web Site: www.southendunited.co.uk

GENERAL INFORMATION

Car Parking: Car park at the ground for 500 cars – Season Ticket holders only. Otherwise use street parking
Coach Parking: Car park at the ground. Coach drivers should contact the club prior to the game
Nearest Railway Station: Prittlewell (¼ mile)
Nearest Bus Station: London Road, Southend
Club Shop: At the ground
Opening Times: Monday to Friday and Matchdays during office hours. Non-Match Saturdays 10.00am to 3.00pm
Telephone No: (01702) 351117
Police Telephone No: (01702) 431212

GROUND INFORMATION

Away Supporters' Entrances & Sections:
North Stand turnstiles for North Stand seating

ADMISSION INFO (2009/2010 PRICES)

Adult Seating: £21.55
Child Seating: £10.75
Concessionary Seating: £14.70
Note: Discounts are available for tickets bought in advance
Programme Price: £3.00

DISABLED INFORMATION

Wheelchairs: 20 spaces in total for Home and Away fans in the disabled section, West Stand
Helpers: One helper admitted per disabled person
Prices: Concessionary prices apply to disabled. Helpers receive complimentary tickets
Disabled Toilets: One available in the disabled area
Commentaries are available for the blind
Contact: 08444 770077 (Bookings are necessary)

Travelling Supporters' Information:
Routes: From the North and West: From the M25 take Junction 29 and follow the A127 to Southend. About 1 mile outside of Southend Town Centre, take the 3rd exit at the roundabout into Victoria Avenue for the ground; From the A13: Follow signs for Southend, turn left into West Road at Westcliff. At the end of West Road turn left into Victoria Avenue – the ground is on the left.

STOCKPORT COUNTY FC

Founded: 1883 (**Entered League**: 1900)
Former Names: Heaton Norris Rovers FC and Heaton Norris FC
Nickname: 'Hatters' 'County'
Ground: Edgeley Park, Hardcastle Road, Edgeley, Stockport SK3 9DD
Ground Capacity: 10,641 (All seats)
Record Attendance: 27,833 (11th February 1950)
Pitch Size: 111 × 72 yards
Colours: Shirts are Blue with a White chest band, shorts are Blue with White trim
Telephone Nº: (0161) 286-8888
Ticket Office: 0871 222-0120
Fax Number: (0161) 429-7392
Web Site: www.stockportcounty.com

GENERAL INFORMATION

Car Parking: Street parking
Coach Parking: By Police direction
Nearest Railway Station: Stockport (5 minutes walk)
Nearest Bus Station: Mersey Square (10 minutes walk)
Club Shop: At the ground
Opening Times: Weekdays 1.00pm – 5.30pm and Saturdays 9.30am – 1.00pm
Telephone Nº: (0161) 286-8899
Police Telephone Nº: (0161) 872-5050

GROUND INFORMATION

Away Supporters' Entrances & Sections:
Railway End turnstiles for Railway End or turnstiles for Popular Side depending on the opponents

ADMISSION INFO (2009/2010 PRICES)

Adult Seating: £17.00 – £18.00
Child Seating: £6.00
Senior Citizen Seating: £12.00
Programme Price: £2.50

DISABLED INFORMATION

Wheelchairs: 16 spaces in total. 10 in the Hardcastle Road Stand, 6 in the Cheadle Stand
Helpers: One helper admitted per disabled fan
Prices: £12.00 for the disabled. Helpers free of charge
Disabled Toilets: Yes
Contact: (0161) 286-8888 (Bookings are necessary)

Travelling Supporters' Information:
Routes: From the North, South and West: Exit the M63 at Junction 11 and join the A560, following signs for Cheadle. After ¼ mile turn right into Edgeley Road and after 1 mile turn right into Caroline Street for the ground; From the East: Take the A6 or A560 into Stockport Town Centre and turn left into Greek Street. Take the 2nd exit into Mercian Way (from the roundabout) then turn left into Caroline Street – the ground is straight ahead.

STOKE CITY FC

Founded: 1863 (**Entered League**: 1888)
Former Name: Stoke FC
Nickname: 'The Potters'
Ground: Britannia Stadium, Stanley Matthews Way, Stoke-on-Trent ST4 4EG
Ground Capacity: 27,500 (All seats)
Record Attendance: 28,218 (5th January 2002)
Pitch Size: 115 × 72 yards
Colours: Red and White striped shirts, White shorts
Telephone Nº: 0871 663-2008
Ticket Office: 0871 663-2007
Fax Number: (01782) 592210
Web Site: www.stokecityfc.com

GENERAL INFORMATION

Car Parking: At the ground (bookings necessary). Also various car parks within 10 minutes walk
Coach Parking: At the ground
Nearest Railway Station: Stoke-on-Trent (1½ miles)
Nearest Bus Station: Glebe Street, Stoke-on-Trent
Club Shop: At the ground and also at the Potteries Shopping Centre in Hanley
Opening Times: Monday to Friday 9.00am – 5.30pm and non-match Saturdays 9.00am–5.00pm. Saturday Matchdays 9.00am to kick-off and Final whistle to 5.30pm. Evening matchdays 9.00am to kick-off and Final whistle to 10.00pm
Telephone Nº: 0871 663-2008
Police Telephone Nº: 08453 302010

GROUND INFORMATION

Away Supporters' Sections: South Stand

ADMISSION INFO (2008/2009 PRICES)

Adult Seating: £25.00 – £42.00
Child Seating: £8.00 – £20.00
Senior Citizen Seating: £19.00 – £29.00
Programme Price: £3.00

DISABLED INFORMATION

Wheelchairs: 112 spaces available in total
Helpers: One helper admitted per disabled person
Prices: £19.00 to £29.00
Disabled Toilets: Available
Commentaries are available – phone for details
Contact: 0871 663-2008 (Bookings are necessary)

Travelling Supporters' Information:
Routes: From the North, South and West: Exit the M6 at Junction 15 and take the A500 to Stoke-on-Trent. At the first exit, take the A34 to Stone and follow signs for Trentham. At the next roundabout, turn left onto Trentham Road (A5035) and carry on until you reach the junction with traffic lights which sits on the southern entrance to Stanley Matthews Way for the ground; From the East: Take the A50 to Stoke-on-Trent and leave at the Longton Exit into Trentham Road (A5035). Stay on Trentham Road until you reach the junction with traffic lights which sits on the southern entrance to Stanley Matthews Way.

SUNDERLAND AFC

Founded: 1879 (**Entered League**: 1890)
Former Names: Sunderland and District Teachers FC
Nickname: 'The Black Cats'
Ground: Stadium of Light, Sunderland SR5 1SU
Ground Capacity: 49,000 (All seats)
Record Attendance: 48,355 (13th April 2002)
Pitch Size: 115 × 75 yards

Colours: Red and White striped shirts, Black shorts
Telephone Nº: (0191) 551-5000
Ticket Office: 0845 671-1973
Fax Number: (0191) 551-5123
Web Site: www.safc.com

GENERAL INFORMATION

Car Parking: Spaces for 1,100 cars (reserved)
Coach Parking: At the ground
Nearest Railway Station: Sunderland (1 mile)
Nearest Bus Station: Town Centre (1 mile)
Club Shop: At the Stadium, plus smaller stores in Sainsburys in Washington and Debenhams in Sunderland
Opening Times: Monday to Saturday 9.00am – 5.00pm
Telephone Nº: (0191) 551-5050
Police Telephone Nº: (0191) 510-2020

GROUND INFORMATION

Away Supporters' Entrances & Sections:
South Stand

ADMISSION INFO (2008/2009 PRICES)

Adult Seating: £22.00 – £33.00
Child Seating: £10.00 or £12.00 (some sections only)
Senior Citizen/Under-22s Seating: £17.00 or £22.00
Note: Prices vary depending on the category of the game. Concessionary prices are not available for away fans
Programme Price: £3.00

DISABLED INFORMATION

Wheelchairs: 180 spaces in total throughout the stadium
Helpers: Admitted
Prices: Normal prices for the disabled. Free for helpers
Disabled Toilets: Available in all stands and Corporate areas
Contact: 0845 671-1973 (Bookings are necessary)

Travelling Supporters' Information:
Routes: From All Parts: Exit the A1 at the A690 Durham/Sunderland exit. After approximately 4 miles turn left onto the A19 (signposted Tyne Tunnel). Keep in the left lane and take the slip road (signposted Washington/Sunderland) onto the bridge over the River Wear. Turn right onto the A1231 (signposted Washington/Sunderland), stay on this road going straight across 4 roundabouts into Sunderland. Continue straight through 2 sets of traffic lights and the Stadium car park is on the right, about 1 mile past the traffic lights.

SWANSEA CITY FC

Founded: 1912 (**Entered League**: 1920)
Former Name: Swansea Town FC (1912-1970)
Nickname: 'The Swans'
Ground: Liberty Stadium, Landore, Swansea, SA1 2FA
Ground Capacity: 20,520 (All seats)
Record Attendance: 32,796 (at the Vetch Field)
Pitch Size: 115 × 74 yards
Colours: White shirts and shorts with Black trim
Telephone Nº: (01792) 616600
Ticket Office: 08700 400004
Fax Number: (01792) 616606
Web Site: www.swanseacity.net

GENERAL INFORMATION

Car Parking: Reserved parking only at the stadium but 3,000 spaces are available in a Park & Ride scheme just off Junction 45 of the M4.
Coach Parking: By Police direction
Nearest Railway Station: Swansea High Street (3 miles)
Nearest Bus Station: Quadrant Depot (4 miles)
Club Shop: At the ground
Opening Times: Monday to Saturday 9.00am – 5.00pm
Telephone Nº: 0871 222-3434
Police Telephone Nº: (01792) 456999

GROUND INFORMATION

Away Supporters' Entrances & Sections:
North Stand

ADMISSION INFO (2009/2010 PRICES)

Adult Seating: £20.00 – £30.00
Child Seating: £10.00
Senior Citizen Seating: £13.00 – £15.00
Programme Price: £3.00

DISABLED INFORMATION

Wheelchairs: 250 spaces available in total for Home and Away fans together with 250 spaces for helpers
Helpers: One helper admitted per wheelchair
Prices: Normal prices apply for the disabled. Free for helpers
Disabled Toilets: Available
There are a number of disabled parking spaces available at the stadium
Contact: (01792) 616402 (Bookings are necessary)

Travelling Supporters' Information:
Routes: From All Parts: Exit the M4 at Junction 45 and follow signs for Swansea (A4067). The stadium is clearly signposted.

SWINDON TOWN FC

Founded: 1881 (**Entered League**: 1920)
Nickname: 'Robins'
Ground: County Ground, County Road, Swindon, SN1 2ED
Ground Capacity: 14,983 (All seats)
Record Attendance: 32,000 (15th January 1972)
Pitch Size: 110 × 73 yards

Colours: Red shirts and shorts
Telephone Nº: 0871 423-6433
Ticket Office: 0871 223-2300
Fax Number: 0844 880-1112
Web Site: www.swindontownfc.co.uk

GENERAL INFORMATION

Car Parking: Town Centre
Coach Parking: Car park adjacent to the ground
Nearest Railway Station: Swindon (½ mile)
Nearest Bus Station: Swindon (½ mile)
Club Shop: The Swindon Town Superstore
Opening Times: Weekdays 9.00am – 5.00pm, Non-Matchday Saturdays 9.00am – 12.00pm and Saturday Matchdays 9.00am to 3.00pm
Telephone Nº: 0844 880-1085
Police Telephone Nº: 0845 408-7000

GROUND INFORMATION

Away Supporters' Entrances & Sections:
Arkell's Stand turnstiles for the Stratton Bank

ADMISSION INFO (2009/2010 PRICES)

Adult Seating: £16.00 – £22.00
Child Seating: £10.00
Concessions Seating: £12.00 – £15.00
Programme Price: £3.00

DISABLED INFORMATION

Wheelchairs: 56 spaces in total for Home and Away fans in disabled section, in front of Arkell's Stand
Helpers: One helper admitted per wheelchair disabled fan
Prices: Please contact the club for details
Disabled Toilets: Available within the disabled area
Commentaries are available for the blind
Contact: 0871 223-2300 (Bookings are necessary)

Travelling Supporters' Information:
Routes: From London, the East and the South: Exit the M4 at Junction 15 and take the A345 into Swindon along Queen's Drive. Take the 3rd exit at 'Magic Roundabout' into County Road; From the West: Exit the M4 at Junction 15 then as above; From the North: Take the M4 or A345/A420/A361 to the County Road roundabout, then as above.

TORQUAY UNITED FC

Founded: 1899 (First Entered League: 1927)
Former Name: Torquay Town FC (1899-1910)
Nickname: 'Gulls'
Ground: Plainmoor Ground, Torquay TQ1 3PS
Ground Capacity: 5,966
Seating Capacity: 2,481
Record Attendance: 21,908 (29th January 1955)

Pitch Size: 112 × 74 yards
Colours: Shirts are Yellow with Royal Blue trim, shorts and socks are Yellow
Telephone Nº: (01803) 328666
Ticket Office: (01803) 328666
Fax Number: (01803) 323976
Web Site: www.torquayunited.com

GENERAL INFORMATION

Car Parking: Street parking
Coach Parking: Lymington Road Coach Station (½ mile)
Nearest Railway Station: Torquay (2 miles)
Nearest Bus Station: Lymington Road (½ mile)
Club Shop: At the ground
Opening Times: Matchdays and during Office Hours
Telephone Nº: (01803) 328666
Police Telephone Nº: 0845 277-7444

GROUND INFORMATION

Away Supporters' Entrances & Sections:
Babbacombe End turnstiles for Babbacombe End

ADMISSION INFO (2009/2010 PRICES)

Adult Standing: £15.00
Adult Seating: £16.00
Concessionary Standing: £12.00 (Under-16s £6.00)
Concessionary Seating: £13.00 (Under-16s £6.00)
Programme Price: £2.50

DISABLED INFORMATION

Wheelchairs: 11 spaces in front of Ellacombe End Stand plus 5 spaces in the Away End.
Helpers: One helper admitted per wheelchair
Prices: Normal prices for the disabled. Free for helpers
Disabled Toilets: 2 available within the Main Stand
Audio facilities are available for the blind
Contact: (01803) 328666 (Bookings necessary for the blind)

Travelling Supporters' Information:
Routes: From the North and East: Take the M5 to the A38 then A380 to Torquay. On entering Torquay, turn left at the 1st set of traffic lights after Riviera Way Retail Park into Hele Road. Following signs for the ground, continue straight on over two mini-roundabouts, go up West Hill Road to the traffic lights, then straight ahead into Warbro Road. The ground is situated on the right after 200 yards.

TOTTENHAM HOTSPUR FC

Founded: 1882 (**Entered League:** 1908)
Former Name: Hotspur FC (1882-1884)
Nickname: 'Spurs'
Ground: White Hart Lane, Bill Nicholson Way, 748 High Road, Tottenham, London N17 0AP
Ground Capacity: 36,240 (All seats)
Record Attendance: 75,038 (5th March 1938)

Pitch Size: 110 × 73 yards
Colours: White shirts with Navy Blue shorts
Telephone Nº: 0844 499-5000
Ticket Office: 0844 844-0102
Fax Number: (020) 8365-5175
Web Site: www.tottenhamhotspur.com

GENERAL INFORMATION

Car Parking: None within ¼ mile of the ground
Coach Parking: Northumberland Park, Leeside Road
Nearest Railway Station: White Hart Lane (nearby) or Northumberland Park
Nearest Tube Station: Seven Sisters (Victoria Line) or Manor House (Piccadilly Line)
Club Shop: Megastore at the ground plus stores in Harlow, Enfield and Chelmsford
Opening Times: Monday to Saturday 9.30am – 5.30pm (open from 10.00am on Monday and Tuesday). Also Sundays 10.00am – 4.00pm
Telephone Nº: 0844 499-5000
Police Telephone Nº: (020) 8801-3443

GROUND INFORMATION

Away Supporters' Entrances & Sections:
Park Lane entrances for South Stand

ADMISSION INFO (2009/2010 PRICES)

Adult Seating: £27.40 – £73.40
Child Seating: £14.70 – £24.50
Senior Citizen Seating: £17.70 – £27.40
Note: Additional discounts are available for members and prices vary depending on the category of the game
Programme Price: £3.00

DISABLED INFORMATION

Wheelchairs: 69 spaces for home fans, 8 for away fans in the disabled areas. Home supporters' area: North Stand West Lower Tier and South Lower; Away Supporters' area: South Stand Lower Tier.
Helpers: One helper admitted per disabled person
Prices: £27.40 – £42.10
Disabled Toilets: 4 available in the North Stand and 2 available in the South Stand
Contact: (020) 8365-5161 (Bookings are necessary)

Travelling Supporters' Information:
Routes: From All Parts: Take the A406 North Circular to Edmonton and at traffic lights follow signs for Tottenham (A1010) into Fore Street for the ground.

TRANMERE ROVERS FC

Founded: 1885 (**Entered League**: 1921)
Former Name: Belmont FC
Nickname: 'Rovers'
Ground: Prenton Park, Prenton Road West, Birkenhead CH42 9PY
Ground Capacity: 16,151 (All seats)
Record Attendance: 24,424 (5th February 1972)

Pitch Size: 110 × 70 yards
Colours: White shirts and shorts
Telephone Nº: 0871 221-2001
Ticket Office: 0871 221-2001
Fax Number: (0151) 608-6114
Web Site: www.tranmererovers.co.uk

GENERAL INFORMATION

Car Parking: Large car park at the ground (£4.00 per car)
Coach Parking: At the ground (£10.00 charge)
Nearest Railway Stations: Hamilton Square, Rock Ferry and Conway Park (approximately 1½ miles)
Nearest Bus Station: Conway Park (Town Centre)
Club Shop: At the ground
Opening Times: Weekdays 9.30am–5.00pm, Matchdays 10.00am– kick-off, non-Saturday matchdays 10.00am–1.00pm
Telephone Nº: 0871 221-2001
Police Telephone Nº: (0151) 709-6010

GROUND INFORMATION

Away Supporters' Entrances & Sections:
Cowshed Stand turnstiles 5-9 – access from Borough Road (Away section capacity: 2,500)

ADMISSION INFO (2009/2010 PRICES)

Adult Seating: £13.00 – £22.00
Child Seating: £5.00
Concessionary Seating (Seniors 60+): £8.50 – £10.50
Young Persons Ticket (Ages 17-22): £8.50 – £13.50
Programme Price: £3.00
Note: Young Person tickets must be purchased from the Ticket Office prior to the game and are only sold upon presentation of photographic proof of age.

DISABLED INFORMATION

Wheelchairs: 28 spaces in total for Home and Away fans in the disabled section, Bebington Paddock
Helpers: One helper admitted per disabled person
Prices: Adults £5.00 Concessions £3.00
Disabled Toilets: 2 available in the disabled section
Contact: 0871 221-2001 (Bookings are necessary)

Travelling Supporters' Information:
Routes: From the North: Take the Mersey Tunnel (Queensway), bear right onto the flyover after the tollbooths and continue on to Borough Road. Continue on Borough Road for approximately 1 mile and the ground is situated on the right; From the South and East: Exit the M53 at Junction 4 and take the 3rd exit at roundabout (B5151). After 2½ miles turn right into Prenton Road West for the ground.

WALSALL FC

Founded: 1888 (**Entered League:** 1892)
Former Name: Walsall Town Swifts FC (1888-1895)
Nickname: 'Saddlers'
Ground: Banks's Stadium, Bescot Crescent, Walsall, West Midlands WS1 4SA
Ground Capacity: 11,300 (All seats)
Record Attendance: 11,037 (11th January 2003)
Pitch Size: 110 × 73 yards

Colours: Red shirts with White shorts
Telephone N°: (01922) 622791
Ticket Office: (01922) 651416 or (01922) 651414
Fax Number: (01922) 613202
Web Site: www.saddlers.co.uk

GENERAL INFORMATION

Car Parking: Car park at the ground
Coach Parking: At the ground
Nearest Railway Station: Bescot (adjacent)
Nearest Bus Station: Bradford Place, Walsall
Club Shop: At the ground and in Bradford Street, Walsall
Opening Times: Weekdays and Matchdays 9.00am–5.00pm
Telephone N°: (01922) 631072 (Bradford Street)
Police Telephone N°: (01922) 638111

GROUND INFORMATION

Away Supporters' Entrances & Sections:
Turnstiles 21-28 for Dains Stand accommodation

ADMISSION INFO (2009/2010 PRICES)

Adult Seating: £14.00 – £20.00
Child Seating: £8.00 – £12.00
Concessionary Seating: £10.00 – £13.00
Note: Prices shown include discounts for advance bookings and savings from Family Tickets are available in some stands
Programme Price: £2.50

DISABLED INFORMATION

Wheelchairs: 30 spaces in total for Home and Away fans in the disabled section, Walsall Bite Size Stand
Helpers: One helper admitted per disabled person
Prices: £18.00 for the wheelchair disabled. Free of charge for helpers
Disabled Toilets: Adjacent to disabled viewing bays
A special Lounge for fans with disabilities is available
Contact: (01922) 651416 (Bookings are necessary)

Travelling Supporters' Information:
Routes: From All Parts: Exit the M6 at Junction 9 turning North towards Walsall onto the A461. After ¼ mile turn right into Wallows Lane and pass over the railway bridge. Then take the 1st right into Bescot Crescent and the ground is ½ mile along on the left adjacent to Bescot Railway Station.

WATFORD FC

Founded: 1881 (**Entered League:** 1920)
Former Names: Formed by the amalgamation of West Herts FC and St. Mary's FC
Nickname: 'Hornets'
Ground: Vicarage Road Stadium, Watford, WD18 0ER
Ground Capacity: 17,598 (All seats)
Record Attendance: 34,099 (3rd February 1969)

Pitch Size: 114 × 73 yards
Colours: Yellow shirts with Black shorts
Telephone Nº: 0844 856-1881
Ticket Office: 0844 856-1881
Fax Number: (01923) 496001
Web Site: www.watfordfc.com

GENERAL INFORMATION

Car Parking: Nearby multi-storey car parks and schools
Coach Parking: By Police direction
Nearest Railway Station: Watford Junction or Watford Tube Station (Metropolitan Line)
Nearest Bus Station: Watford Town Centre
Club Shop: The Hornets Shop at Vicarage Road Stadium
Opening Times: Monday to Saturday 9.00am to 5.30pm
Telephone Nº: 0844 856-1881
Police Telephone Nº: (01923) 472000

GROUND INFORMATION

Away Supporters' Entrances & Sections:
Vicarage Road End entrances and accommodation

ADMISSION INFO (2009/2010 PRICES)

Adult Seating: £10.00 – £25.00
Child Seating: £1.00 – £10.00
Senior Citizen Seating: £10.00 – £15.00
Programme Price: £3.00

DISABLED INFORMATION

Wheelchairs: 40 spaces in total in the disabled sections, South East Corner and North Stand
Helpers: One helper admitted per disabled person
Prices: £10.00 – £20.00 for the disabled. Free for helpers
Disabled Toilets: Adjacent to disabled enclosures
Commentaries available around the ground – no charge
Contact: 0844 856-1881 (Bookings in advance helpful)

Travelling Supporters' Information:
Routes: From the North: Exit the M1 at Junction 5 and take the new road (A4008) towards Watford Town Centre. This will take you around the ring road, follow signs for Watford General Hospital. The ground is next to the hospital; From the South: Exit M1 at Junction 5 (then as North); From the East: Exit the M25 at Junction 21A and join the M1 at Junction 6. Exit at Junction 5 (then as North); From the West: Exit the M25 at Junction 19 and take the third exit off the roundabout onto the A411 (Hempstead Road) signposted for Watford. Continue for approximately two miles and go straight on at the roundabout (enter the right-hand lane) for the next roundabout and take the third exit into Rickmansworth Road. Take the second turning on the left into Cassio Road. Go through the traffic lights into Merton Road and follow signs for Watford General Hospital into Vicarage Road.

WEST BROMWICH ALBION FC

Founded: 1879 (**Entered League**: 1888)
Former Name: West Bromwich Strollers (1879-1880)
Nickname: 'Throstles' 'Baggies' 'Albion'
Ground: The Hawthorns, Halfords Lane,
West Bromwich, West Midlands B71 4LF
Ground Capacity: 26,346 (All seats)
Record Attendance: 64,815 (6th March 1937)
Pitch Size: 115 × 74 yards
Colours: Navy Blue & White striped shirts, White shorts
Telephone Nº: 0871 271-1100
Ticket Office: 0871 271-9780
Fax Number: 0871 271-9861
Web Site: www.wba.co.uk

GENERAL INFORMATION

Car Parking: Halfords Lane Car Parks, East Stand Car Park and several independent car parks
Coach Parking: At the ground
Nearest Railway Station: Hawthorns (200 yards) or Rolfe Street, Smethwick (1½ miles)
Nearest Midland Metro: Hawthorns (200 yards)
Nearest Bus Station: West Bromwich Town Centre
Club Shop: At the ground and at the Merry Hill Centre
Opening Times: Weekdays 9.00am – 5.00pm and Saturday Matchdays 9.00am – 2.45pm
Telephone Nº: 0871 271-9790

GROUND INFORMATION

Away Supporters' Entrances & Sections:
Smethwick End 'A' turnstiles

ADMISSION INFO (2009/2010 PRICES)

Adult Seating: £25.00 – £40.00
Child Seating: £10.00 – £20.00
Senior Citizen Seating: £15.00 – £25.00
Student Seating: £15.00 – £25.00
Programme Price: £3.00

DISABLED INFORMATION

Wheelchairs: 150 spaces in total in the disabled sections, Birmingham Road End, Smethwick End and the East Stand
Helpers: One helper admitted per disabled person (subject to availability of space)
Prices: £10.00 – £20.00 for the disabled. Free for helpers
Disabled Toilets: Available within disabled section
Contact: 0871 271-1100 (Bookings are necessary)

Travelling Supporters' Information:
Routes: From All Parts: Exit the M5 at Junction 1 and follow Matchday signs for the ground. The matchday traffic plan has made the "obvious" route via the A41 unusable for home games.

WEST HAM UNITED FC

Founded: 1895 (**Entered League**: 1919)
Former Name: Thames Iron Works FC
Nickname: 'Hammers'
Ground: Boleyn Ground, Green Street, Upton Park, London E13 9AZ
Ground Capacity: 35,303 (All seats)
Record Attendance: 42,322 (17th October 1970)

Pitch Size: 110 × 70 yards
Colours: Claret and Blue shirts with White shorts
Telephone Nº: (020) 8548-2748
Ticket Office: 0870 112-2700
Fax Number: (020) 8548-2758
Web Site: www.whufc.com

GENERAL INFORMATION

Car Parking: Street parking
Coach Parking: By Police direction
Nearest Railway Station: Barking
Nearest Tube Station: Upton Park (5 minutes walk)
Club Shops: At the Stadium and also at Lakeside
Opening Times: Weekdays and Matchdays 9.30am–5.00pm
Telephone Nº: (020) 8548-2794 (Stadium Store); (01708) 890258 (Lakeside Store)
Mail-Order Nº: 0870 112-2700
Police Telephone Nº: (020) 8593-8232

GROUND INFORMATION

Away Supporters' Entrances & Sections:
Priory Road entrance for the Centenary Stand

ADMISSION INFO (2009/2010 PRICES)

Adult Seating: £35.00 – £66.00
Child Seating: £17.00 – £34.50 (Discounts for Members)
Senior Citizen Seating: £17.50 – £31.50
Note: Prices vary depending on the category of the game
Programme Price: £3.00

DISABLED INFORMATION

Wheelchairs: 150 spaces for home fans, 12 spaces for away fans in the disabled area, Centenary Stand
Helpers: Admitted
Prices: £17.00 for the disabled. Free of charge for helpers
Disabled Toilets: 12 available
Contact: Gina Allen (020) 8548-2725 (Bookings necessary)

Travelling Supporters' Information:
Routes: From the North and West: Take the North Circular (A406) to the A124 (East Ham) then along Barking Road for approximately 1½ miles until approaching the traffic lights at the crossroad. Turn right into Green Street, the ground is on the right-hand side; From the South: Take the Blackwall Tunnel and the A13 to Canning Town. Follow signs for East Ham (A124). After 1¾ miles turn left into Green Street; From the East: Take the A13 and turn right onto the A117 at the crossroads. After approximately 1 mile turn left at the crossroads onto the A124. Turn right after ¾ mile into Green Street for the ground.

WIGAN ATHLETIC FC

Founded: 1932 (**Entered League**: 1978)
Nickname: 'Latics'
Ground: DW Stadium, Robin Park, Newtown, Wigan, Lancashire WN5 0UZ
Ground Capacity: 25,138 (All seats)
Record Attendance: 25,133 (11th May 2008)
Pitch Size: 115 × 74 yards

Colours: Blue and White striped shirts, Blue shorts
Telephone Nº: (01942) 774000
Ticket Office: 0871 66-33-552
Fax Number: (01942) 770477
Web Site: www.wiganathletic.tv

GENERAL INFORMATION

Car Parking: 2,500 spaces available at the ground (£4.00 for cars, £10.00 for minibuses, £20.00 for coaches)
Coach Parking: At the ground
Nearest Railway Station: Wallgate and Wigan North Western (1 mile)
Nearest Bus Station: Wigan
Club Shop: At the DW Stadium
Opening Times: Weekdays 9.00am to 5.00pm and Matchdays 10.00am – 4.00pm
Police Telephone Nº: (0161) 872-5050

GROUND INFORMATION

Away Supporters' Entrances & Sections: North Stand

ADMISSION INFO (2009/2010 PRICES)

Adult Seating: £20.00 – £30.00
Child/Senior Citizen Seating: £15.00 – £20.00
JJ's Club: £5.00 – £10.00 (Children only)
Note: Prices vary depending on the category of the game
Programme Price: £3.00

DISABLED INFORMATION

Wheelchairs: 25 spaces available in each stand
Helpers: One helper admitted per disabled supporter
Prices: £15.00 – £20.00 for each disabled fan + a helper
Disabled Toilets: Available in every stand
Contact: (01942) 774000 (Bookings are necessary)

Travelling Supporters' Information:
Routes: From North: Exit M6 at Junction 27, turn left at end of slip road then right at T-junction, signposted Shevington. After 1 mile turn left at the mini-roundabout into Old Lane (B5375). After approx. 2 miles winding through countryside turn right at traffic lights into Scot Lane. Stadium is next left; From South & West: Exit M6 at Junction 25 follow signs for Wigan (A49). After approx. 2 miles a complex junction is reached, keep in left-hand lane (McDonalds on right). Turn left at traffic light filter lane into Robin Park Road. Turn right at third set of traffic lights and follow road to stadium; From East: Exit M61 Junction 6, take 1st exit at roundabout. At next roundabout take 1st left into Chorley Road. Follow signs for Wigan B5238, first turning right then left at Aspull Roundabout. After 2 miles turn right at traffic lights after Earl of Balcarres Pub to face Tesco. Turn left at lights, keep in left lane turn left at next lights with the Quality Hotel on the corner. Follow ring road, get into second lane from right as road bears right into Caroline Street, signposted Orrell. Continue on ring road as it bears left passing B&Q on left, pass Wigan Pier on right and as road goes under railway bridge get into right hand lane to turn right at lights into Robin Park Road. Then South & West.

WOLVERHAMPTON WANDERERS FC

Founded: 1877 (**Entered League**: 1888)
Former Names: Formed by the amalgamation of St. Luke's FC and The Wanderers Football and Cricket Club in 1879. St. Luke's is considered the start of the club
Nickname: 'Wolves'
Ground: Molineux Stadium, Waterloo Road, Wolverhampton WV1 4QR
Ground Capacity: 28,576 (All seats)
Record Attendance: 61,315 (11th February 1939)
Pitch Size: 110 × 75 yards
Colours: Gold shirts with Black shorts
Telephone Nº: 0871 880-8442
Ticket Office: 0871 880-8433
Fax Number: (01902) 687006
Web Site: www.wolves.co.uk

GENERAL INFORMATION

Car Parking: Around West Park, Newhampton Road and rear of the Stan Cullis Stand. Also in City Centre (5 minutes walk)
Coach Parking: By Police direction
Nearest Railway Station: Wolverhampton (¾ mile)
Nearest Bus Station: Wolverhampton (¾ mile)
Club Shop: At the ground and in the City Centre
Opening Times: Daily from 9.00am – 5.00pm
Telephone Nº: 0871 880-8442
Police Telephone Nº: (01902) 649000

GROUND INFORMATION

Away Supporters' Entrances & Sections:
Jack Harris turnstiles for Block 5 or Steve Bull Stand Lower Tier (turnstiles for Block 3)

ADMISSION INFO (2009/2010 PRICES)

Adult Seating: £24.00 – £40.00
Senior Citizen Seating: £14.00 – £34.00
Under-17s Seating: £8.00 – £15.00
Under-12s Seating: £10.00 (with a paying adult)
Programme Price: £3.00

DISABLED INFORMATION

Wheelchairs: 104 spaces in total in the disabled sections, Stan Cullis Stand and Billy Wright Family Enclosure
Helpers: Admitted
Prices: Please contact the club for details
Disabled Toilets: At both ends of the Stan Cullis Stand
Commentaries for the blind available from local radio
Contact: 0870 442-0123 (Lindsey Beckett)
(Bookings are necessary)

Travelling Supporters' Information:
Routes: From North: Exit M6 Junction 12. At island take 3rd exit onto A5 for Wolverhampton. At next island turn left onto A449. After 6 miles A449 passes under M54, carry straight on and at 6th roundabout (Five Ways) take 3rd exit into Waterloo Road. Molineux is 1 mile straight on; From South West: Exit M5 Junction 2, follow signs for Wolverhampton on A4123 for 8 miles to ring road. Turn left on ring road (follow Molineux Centre signs). Take 2nd exit at next 2 islands * Pass Bank's Brewery and Swimming Baths on left and turn left at next set of traffic lights. Molineux is 500 yards on right; From South/East: Exit M6 Junction 10, take A454 (via Willenhall) to Wolverhampton ring road. At first ring road island take 4th exit (A449 to Stafford). Straight on at next 2 sets of traffic lights. Filter right at third set of lights (Waterloo Road). Molineux is 500 yards on right; From West: Take A41 to Wolverhampton ring road roundabout. Turn left into the ring road. Then as from the South West *

WYCOMBE WANDERERS FC

Founded: 1884 (**Entered League:** 1993)
Nickname: 'The Blues' 'The Chairboys'
Ground: Adams Park, Hillbottom Road, Sands, High Wycombe HP12 4HJ
Ground Capacity: 10,000
Seating Capacity: 8,250
Record Attendance: 9,971 (10th January 2007)
Pitch Size: 115 × 75 yards
Colours: Navy and Light Blue quarters with Navy shorts
Telephone Nº: (01494) 472100
Ticket Office: (01494) 441118
Fax Number: (01494) 527633
Web Site: www.wycombewanderers.co.uk

GENERAL INFORMATION

Car Parking: Car park at the ground
Coach Parking: Car park at the ground
Nearest Railway Station: High Wycombe
Nearest Bus Station: High Wycombe
Club Shop: At the ground
Opening Times: Weekdays and Matchdays
Telephone Nº: (01494) 472100
Police Telephone Nº: (01494) 465888

GROUND INFORMATION

Away Supporters' Entrances & Sections:
Dreams Stand (seating only)

ADMISSION INFO (2009/2010 PRICES)

Adult Standing: £13.00–£15.00 **Seating:** £16.00–£21.00
Under-16s Standing: £5.00–£7.00 (**Under-7s:** £4 – £6)
Under-16s Seating: £5.00 – £16.00 (**Under-7s:** £4 – £15)
Senior Citizen Standing: £11 – £13 (**Seating:** £13–£17)
Student Standing: £9.00 – £11.00 (**Seating:** £12–£16)
Note: A £2.00 discount is available for pre-booked tickets
Programme Price: £2.50

DISABLED INFORMATION

Wheelchairs: 50 spaces in total available in the disabled section of the Family Stand
Helpers: One helper admitted per wheelchair
Prices: Free for the disabled. Full price for helpers
Disabled Toilets: Available in the New Family Stand
Commentaries are available for 5 people
Contact: (01494) 472100 (Bookings are necessary)

Travelling Supporters' Information:
Routes: From All Parts: Exit the M40 at Junction 4 and take the A4010 following Aylesbury signs. Go straight on at 3 mini-roundabouts then bear sharp left at the 4th roundabout into Lane End Road. Fork right into Hillbottom Road at the next roundabout. The ground is at the end of the road. Hillbottom Road is on the Sands Industrial Estate; From the Town Centre: Take the A40 West and after 1½ miles turn left into Chapel Lane (after the traffic lights). Turn right then right again at the mini-roundabout into Lane End Road – then as above.

YEOVIL TOWN FC

Founded: 1895
Former Names: Yeovil & Petters United FC
Nickname: 'Glovers'
Ground: Huish Park Stadium, Lufton Way, Yeovil, Somerset BA22 8YF
Ground Capacity: 9,715
Seating Capacity: 5,485

Record Attendance: 9,527 (25th April 2008)
Pitch Size: 115 × 72 yards
Colours: Green and White shirts with Green shorts
Telephone No: (01935) 423662
Ticket Office No: (01935) 847888
Fax Number: (01935) 473956
Web site: www.ytfc.net

GENERAL INFORMATION

Car Parking: Spaces for 1,000 cars at the ground
Coach Parking: At the ground
Nearest Railway Station: Yeovil Pen Mill (2½ miles) and Yeovil Junction (3½ miles)
Nearest Bus Station: Yeovil (2 miles)
Club Shop: At the ground
Opening Times: Weekdays 9.00am – 5.00pm and Matchdays 10.00am – 3.00pm
Telephone No: (01935) 423662
Police Telephone No: (01935) 415291

GROUND INFORMATION

Away Supporters' Entrances & Sections:
Copse Road End (turnstiles 13-16) and Cowlin Stand (turnstile 12)

ADMISSION INFO (2009/2010 PRICES)

Adult Standing: £17.00
Adult Seating: £17.00 – £20.00
Child Standing: £5.00
Child Seating: £5.00 – £6.00
Senior Citizen Standing: £12.00
Senior Citizen Seating: £13.00 – £17.00
Note: Discounts are available for tickets purchased in advance
Programme Price: £2.50

DISABLED INFORMATION

Wheelchairs: 15 spaces for home fans, 5 spaces for away fans
Helpers: Admitted free of charge
Prices: Please phone the club for information
Disabled Toilets: Two are available
Contact: (01935) 847888 (Bookings are recommended)

Travelling Supporters' Information:
Routes: From London: Take the M3 and A303 to Cartgate Roundabout. Enter Yeovil on the A3088. Exit left at the 1st roundabout then straight over the next two roundabouts into Western Avenue. Cross the next roundabout then turn left into Copse Road, where supporters' parking is sited; From the North: Exit the M5 at Junction 25 and take the A358 (Ilminster) and A303 (Eastbound) entering Yeovil on the A3088. Then as above.

F.A. Premier League 2008/2009 Season	Arsenal	Aston Villa	Blackburn Rovers	Bolton Wanderers	Chelsea	Everton	Fulham	Hull City	Liverpool	Manchester City	Manchester United	Middlesbrough	Newcastle Unitd	Portsmouth	Stoke City	Sunderland	Tottenham Hotspur	West Bromwich Albion	West Ham United	Wigan Athletic
Arsenal		0-2	4-0	1-0	1-4	3-1	0-0	1-2	1-1	2-0	2-1	2-0	3-0	1-0	4-1	0-0	4-4	1-0	0-0	1-0
Aston Villa	2-2		3-2	4-2	0-1	3-3	0-0	1-0	0-0	4-2	0-0	1-2	1-0	0-0	2-2	2-1	1-2	2-1	1-1	0-0
Blackburn Rovers	0-4	0-2		2-2	0-2	0-0	1-0	1-1	1-3	2-2	0-2	1-1	3-0	2-0	3-0	1-2	2-1	0-0	1-1	2-0
Bolton Wanderers	1-3	1-1	0-0		0-2	0-1	1-3	1-1	0-2	2-0	0-1	4-1	1-0	2-1	3-1	0-0	3-2	0-0	2-1	0-1
Chelsea	1-2	2-0	2-0	4-3		0-0	3-1	0-0	0-1	1-0	1-1	2-0	0-0	4-0	2-1	5-0	1-1	2-0	1-1	2-1
Everton	1-1	2-3	2-3	3-0	0-0		1-0	2-0	0-2	1-2	1-1	1-1	2-2	0-3	3-1	3-0	0-0	2-0	3-1	4-0
Fulham	1-0	3-1	1-2	2-1	2-2	0-2		0-1	0-1	1-1	2-0	3-0	2-1	3-1	1-0	0-0	2-1	2-0	1-2	2-0
Hull City	1-3	0-1	1-2	0-1	0-3	2-2	2-1		1-3	2-2	0-1	2-1	1-1	0-0	1-2	1-4	1-2	2-2	1-0	0-5
Liverpool	4-4	5-0	4-0	3-0	2-0	1-1	0-0	2-2		1-1	2-1	2-1	3-0	1-0	0-0	2-0	3-1	3-0	0-0	3-2
Manchester City	3-0	2-0	3-1	1-0	1-3	0-1	1-3	5-1	2-3		0-1	1-0	2-1	6-0	3-0	1-0	1-2	4-2	3-0	1-0
Manchester United	0-0	3-2	2-1	2-0	3-0	1-0	3-0	4-3	1-4	2-0		1-0	1-1	2-0	5-0	1-0	5-2	4-0	2-0	1-0
Middlesbrough	1-1	1-1	0-0	1-3	0-5	0-1	0-0	3-1	2-0	2-0	0-2		0-0	1-1	2-1	1-1	2-1	0-1	1-1	0-0
Newcastle United	1-3	2-0	1-2	1-0	0-2	0-0	0-1	1-2	1-5	2-2	1-2	3-1		0-0	2-2	1-1	2-1	2-1	2-2	2-2
Portsmouth	0-3	0-1	3-2	1-0	0-1	2-1	1-1	2-2	2-3	2-0	0-1	2-1	0-3		2-1	3-1	2-0	2-2	1-4	1-2
Stoke City	2-1	3-2	1-0	2-0	0-2	2-3	0-0	1-1	0-0	1-0	0-1	1-0	1-1	2-2		1-0	2-1	1-0	0-1	2-0
Sunderland	1-1	1-2	0-0	1-4	2-3	0-2	1-0	1-0	0-1	0-3	1-2	2-0	2-1	1-2	2-0		1-1	4-0	0-1	1-2
Tottenham Hotspur	0-0	1-2	1-0	2-0	1-0	0-1	0-0	0-1	2-1	2-1	0-0	4-0	1-0	1-1	3-1	1-2		1-0	1-0	0-0
West Bromwich Albion	1-3	1-2	2-2	1-1	0-3	1-2	1-0	0-3	0-2	2-1	0-5	3-0	2-3	1-1	0-2	3-0	2-0		3-2	3-1
West Ham United	0-2	0-1	4-1	1-3	0-1	1-3	3-1	2-0	0-3	1-0	0-1	2-1	3-1	0-0	2-1	2-0	0-2	0-0		2-1
Wigan Athletic	1-4	0-4	3-0	0-0	0-1	1-0	0-0	1-0	1-1	2-1	1-2	0-1	2-1	1-0	0-0	1-1	1-0	2-1	0-1	

Football League Championship 2008/2009 Season	Barnsley	Birmingham City	Blackpool	Bristol City	Burnley	Cardiff City	Charlton Athletic	Coventry City	Crystal Palace	Derby County	Doncaster Rovers	Ipswich Town	Norwich City	Nottingham Forest	Plymouth Argyle	Preston North End	Queen's Park Rangers	Reading	Sheffield United	Sheffield Wednesday	Southampton	Swansea City	Watford	Wolverhampton Wanderers
Barnsley		1-1	0-1	0-0	3-2	0-1	0-0	1-2	3-1	2-0	4-1	1-2	0-0	1-1	2-0	1-1	2-1	0-1	1-2	2-1	0-1	1-3	2-1	1-1
Birmingham City	2-0		0-1	1-0	1-1	1-1	3-2	0-1	1-0	1-0	1-0	2-1	1-1	2-0	1-1	1-2	1-0	1-3	1-0	3-1	1-0	0-0	3-2	2-0
Blackpool	1-0	2-0		0-1	0-1	1-1	2-0	1-1	2-2	3-2	2-3	0-1	2-0	1-1	0-1	1-3	0-3	2-2	1-3	0-2	1-1	1-1	0-2	2-2
Bristol City	2-0	1-2	0-0		1-2	1-1	2-1	2-0	1-0	1-1	4-1	1-1	1-0	2-2	2-2	1-1	1-1	1-4	0-0	1-1	2-0	0-0	1-1	2-2
Burnley	1-2	1-1	2-0	4-0		2-2	2-1	1-1	4-2	3-0	0-0	0-3	2-0	5-0	0-0	3-1	1-0	1-0	1-0	2-4	3-2	0-2	3-2	1-0
Cardiff City	3-1	1-2	2-0	0-0	3-1		2-0	2-1	2-1	4-1	3-0	0-3	2-2	2-0	1-0	2-0	0-0	2-2	0-3	2-0	2-1	2-2	2-1	1-2
Charlton Athletic	1-3	0-0	2-2	0-2	1-1	2-2		1-2	1-0	2-2	1-2	2-1	4-2	0-2	2-0	0-0	2-2	4-2	2-5	1-2	0-0	2-0	2-3	1-3
Coventry City	1-1	1-0	2-1	0-3	1-3	0-2	0-0		0-2	1-1	1-0	2-2	2-0	2-2	0-1	0-0	1-0	0-0	1-2	2-0	4-1	1-1	2-3	2-1
Crystal Palace	3-0	0-0	0-1	4-2	0-0	0-2	1-0	1-1		1-0	2-1	1-4	3-1	1-2	1-2	2-1	0-0	0-0	0-0	1-1	3-0	2-0	0-0	0-1
Derby County	0-0	1-1	4-1	2-1	1-1	1-1	1-0	2-1	1-2		0-1	0-1	3-1	1-1	2-1	2-2	0-2	0-2	2-1	3-0	0-1	2-2	1-0	2-3
Doncaster Rovers	0-1	0-2	0-0	1-0	2-1	1-1	0-1	1-0	2-0	2-1		1-0	1-1	0-0	1-0	0-2	2-0	0-1	0-2	1-0	0-2	0-0	1-2	0-1
Ipswich Town	3-0	0-1	1-1	3-1	1-1	1-2	1-1	2-1	1-1	2-0	1-3		3-2	2-1	0-0	1-2	2-0	2-0	1-1	1-1	0-3	2-2	0-0	0-2
Norwich City	4-0	1-1	1-1	1-2	1-1	2-0	1-0	1-2	1-2	1-2	2-1	2-0		2-3	1-0	2-2	0-1	0-2	1-0	0-1	2-2	2-3	2-0	5-2
Nottingham Forest	1-0	1-1	0-0	3-2	1-2	0-1	0-0	1-0	0-2	1-3	2-4	1-1	1-2		2-0	2-1	2-2	0-0	0-1	2-1	3-1	1-1	3-2	0-1
Plymouth Argyle	1-2	0-1	1-2	0-2	1-2	2-1	2-2	4-0	1-3	0-3	0-3	1-3	1-2	1-0		1-0	1-1	2-2	2-2	4-0	2-0	0-1	2-1	2-2
Preston North End	2-1	1-0	0-1	2-0	2-1	6-0	2-1	2-1	2-0	2-0	1-0	3-2	1-0	2-1	1-1		2-1	2-1	0-0	1-1	2-3	0-2	2-0	1-3
Queen's Park Rangers	2-1	1-0	1-1	2-1	1-2	1-0	2-1	1-1	0-0	0-2	2-0	1-3	0-1	2-1	0-0	3-2		0-0	0-0	3-2	4-1	1-0	0-0	1-0
Reading	0-0	1-2	1-0	0-2	3-1	1-1	2-2	3-1	4-2	3-0	2-1	0-1	2-0	0-1	2-0	0-0	0-0		0-1	6-0	1-2	4-0	4-0	1-0
Sheffield United	2-1	2-1	2-2	3-0	2-3	0-0	3-1	1-1	2-2	4-2	0-1	2-0	1-0	0-0	2-0	1-0	3-0	0-2		1-2	0-0	1-0	2-1	1-3
Sheffield Wednesday	0-1	1-1	1-1	0-0	4-1	1-0	4-1	0-1	2-0	0-1	1-0	0-0	3-2	1-0	0-1	1-1	1-0	1-2	1-0		2-0	0-0	2-0	0-1
Southampton	0-0	1-2	0-1	0-1	2-2	1-0	2-3	1-1	1-0	1-1	1-2	2-2	2-0	0-2	0-0	3-1	0-0	1-1	1-2	1-1		2-2	0-3	1-2
Swansea City	2-2	2-3	0-1	1-0	1-1	2-2	1-1	0-0	1-3	1-1	3-1	3-0	2-1	3-1	1-0	4-1	0-0	2-0	1-1	1-1	3-0		3-1	3-1
Watford	1-1	0-1	3-4	2-4	3-0	2-2	1-0	2-1	2-0	3-1	1-1	2-1	2-1	2-1	1-2	2-1	3-0	2-2	0-2	2-2	2-2	2-0		2-3
Wolverhampton Wanderers	2-0	1-1	2-0	2-0	2-0	2-2	2-1	2-1	2-1	3-0	1-0	0-0	3-3	5-1	0-1	1-3	1-0	0-3	1-1	4-1	3-0	2-1	3-1	

Football League League One 2008/2009 Season	Brighton & Hove Albion	Bristol Rovers	Carlisle United	Cheltenham Town	Colchester United	Crewe Alexandra	Hartlepool United	Hereford United	Huddersfield Town	Leeds United	Leicester City	Leyton Orient	Millwall	MK Dons	Northampton Town	Oldham Athletic	Peterborough United	Scunthorpe United	Southend United	Stockport County	Swindon Town	Tranmere Rovers	Walsall	Yeovil Town
Brighton & Hove Albion		1-1	0-2	3-3	1-2	0-4	2-1	0-0	0-1	0-2	3-2	0-0	4-1	2-4	1-1	3-1	2-4	1-4	1-3	1-0	2-3	0-0	0-1	5-0
Bristol Rovers	1-2		2-3	3-2	0-0	0-0	4-1	6-1	1-2	2-2	0-1	2-1	4-2	1-2	1-0	2-0	0-1	1-2	4-2	2-0	2-2	2-0	1-3	3-0
Carlisle United	3-1	1-1		1-0	0-2	4-2	0-1	1-2	3-0	0-2	1-2	1-3	2-0	3-2	1-1	1-1	3-3	1-1	2-1	1-2	1-1	1-2	1-1	4-1
Cheltenham Town	2-2	2-1	1-1		4-3	1-0	2-0	2-3	1-2	0-1	0-4	0-1	1-3	3-5	0-1	1-1	3-6	1-2	0-0	2-2	2-0	1-0	0-0	1-0
Colchester United	0-1	0-1	5-0	3-1		0-1	1-1	1-2	0-0	0-1	0-1	1-0	1-2	0-3	2-1	2-2	0-1	0-0	0-1	1-0	3-2	0-1	0-2	1-0
Crewe Alexandra	1-2	1-1	1-2	1-2	2-0		0-0	2-1	3-1	2-3	0-3	0-2	0-1	2-2	1-3	0-3	1-1	3-2	3-4	0-3	1-0	2-1	2-1	2-0
Hartlepool United	1-0	1-1	2-2	4-1	4-2	1-4		4-2	5-3	0-1	2-2	0-1	2-3	1-3	2-0	3-3	1-2	2-3	3-0	0-1	3-3	2-1	2-2	0-0
Hereford United	1-2	0-3	1-0	3-0	0-2	2-0	1-1		0-1	2-0	1-3	2-1	0-2	0-1	0-2	5-0	0-1	1-2	0-1	0-1	1-1	2-2	0-0	1-2
Huddersfield Town	2-2	1-1	1-0	2-2	2-2	3-2	1-1	2-0		1-0	2-3	0-1	1-2	1-3	3-2	1-1	1-0	2-0	0-1	1-1	2-1	1-2	2-1	0-0
Leeds United	3-1	2-2	0-2	2-0	1-2	5-2	4-1	1-0	1-2		1-1	2-1	2-0	2-0	3-0	0-2	3-1	3-2	2-0	1-0	1-0	3-1	3-0	4-0
Leicester City	0-0	2-1	2-2	4-0	1-1	2-1	1-0	2-1	4-2	1-0		3-0	0-1	2-0	0-0	0-0	4-0	2-2	3-0	1-1	1-1	3-1	2-2	1-0
Leyton Orient	2-1	1-2	0-0	1-2	2-1	1-0	1-0	2-1	1-1	2-2	1-3		0-0	1-2	1-3	2-1	2-3	2-2	1-1	0-3	1-2	0-1	0-1	0-1
Millwall	0-1	3-2	1-0	2-0	0-1	0-0	2-0	1-0	2-1	3-1	0-1	2-1		0-4	1-0	2-3	2-0	1-2	1-1	1-0	1-1	1-0	3-1	1-1
MK Dons	2-0	2-1	3-1	3-1	1-1	2-2	3-1	3-0	1-1	3-1	2-2	1-2	0-1		1-0	6-2	1-2	0-2	2-0	1-2	1-2	1-0	0-1	3-0
Northampton Town	2-2	0-0	1-0	4-2	1-2	5-1	1-0	2-1	1-1	2-1	1-2	1-1	0-0	0-1		0-1	1-1	3-3	2-3	4-0	3-4	1-1	0-2	3-0
Oldham Athletic	1-1	0-2	0-0	4-0	0-1	1-1	2-1	4-0	1-1	1-1	1-1	1-1	4-3	2-0	2-1		1-2	3-0	1-1	3-1	0-0	0-2	3-2	0-2
Peterborough United	0-0	5-4	1-0	1-1	2-1	4-2	1-2	2-0	4-0	2-0	2-0	3-0	1-0	0-0	1-0	2-2		2-1	1-2	1-0	2-2	2-2	1-0	1-3
Scunthorpe United	2-0	0-2	2-1	3-0	3-0	3-0	3-0	3-0	1-2	1-2	1-2	2-1	3-2	0-1	4-4	2-0	1-0		1-1	2-1	3-3	1-1	1-1	2-0
Southend United	0-2	1-0	3-0	2-0	3-3	0-1	3-2	1-0	0-1	1-0	0-2	3-0	0-1	0-2	1-0	1-2	1-0	2-0		1-1	2-1	2-1	2-0	0-1
Stockport County	2-0	3-1	3-0	1-0	1-2	4-3	2-1	4-1	1-1	1-3	0-0	0-1	2-2	0-1	1-1	3-1	1-3	0-3	3-1		1-1	0-0	1-2	0-0
Swindon Town	0-2	2-1	1-1	2-2	1-3	0-0	0-1	3-0	1-3	1-3	2-2	0-1	1-2	1-1	2-1	2-0	2-2	4-2	3-0	1-1		3-1	3-2	2-3
Tranmere Rovers	1-0	2-0	4-1	2-0	3-4	2-0	1-0	2-1	3-1	2-1	2-0	0-0	1-3	1-1	4-1	0-1	1-1	2-0	2-2	2-1	1-0		2-1	1-1
Walsall	3-0	0-5	2-1	1-1	2-0	1-1	2-3	1-1	2-3	1-0	1-4	0-2	1-2	0-3	3-1	1-2	1-2	2-1	5-2	1-0	2-1	0-1		2-0
Yeovil Town	1-1	2-2	1-1	1-1	0-2	3-2	2-3	2-2	1-0	1-1	0-2	0-0	2-0	0-0	1-0	2-2	0-1	1-2	1-2	2-4	1-0	1-0	1-1	

Football League League Two 2008/2009 Season	Accrington Stanley	Aldershot Town	Barnet	Bournemouth	Bradford City	Brentford	Bury	Chester City	Chesterfield	Dagenham & Redbridge	Darlington	Exeter City	Gillingham	Grimsby Town	Lincoln City	Luton Town	Macclesfield Town	Morecambe	Notts County	Port Vale	Rochdale	Rotherham United	Shrewsbury Town	Wycombe Wanderers
Accrington Stanley		0-1	1-1	3-0	2-3	1-1	1-2	0-1	1-0	0-0	1-0	2-1	0-2	3-1	0-2	0-0	2-0	1-0	1-1	2-0	1-3	1-3	2-1	0-1
Aldershot Town	3-1		1-1	1-1	3-2	1-1	3-3	2-2	1-1	1-2	2-1	1-0	2-1	2-2	2-0	2-1	1-1	0-2	2-2	1-0	2-4	0-1	0-0	3-2
Barnet	2-1	0-3		1-0	4-1	0-1	1-2	3-1	1-3	1-1	0-1	0-1	2-2	3-3	3-2	1-1	1-3	1-1	0-4	1-2	2-1	2-0	0-0	1-1
Bournemouth	1-0	2-0	0-2		4-1	0-1	2-0	1-0	1-1	2-1	3-1	0-1	1-1	2-1	0-1	1-1	0-1	0-0	0-1	0-0	4-0	0-0	1-0	3-1
Bradford City	1-1	5-0	3-3	1-3		1-1	1-0	0-0	3-2	1-1	0-0	4-1	2-2	2-0	1-1	1-1	1-0	4-0	2-1	0-1	2-0	3-0	0-0	1-0
Brentford	3-0	3-0	1-0	2-0	2-1		1-0	3-0	0-1	2-1	1-1	1-1	1-1	4-0	1-1	2-0	1-0	3-1	1-1	2-0	1-2	0-0	1-1	3-3
Bury	1-0	2-1	1-0	1-0	1-0	1-0		1-1	1-2	2-2	2-2	0-1	4-0	0-2	3-1	1-2	3-0	2-1	2-0	3-0	2-1	1-2	2-1	0-0
Chester City	2-0	0-1	5-1	0-2	0-0	3-0	1-1		1-3	2-2	1-2	0-0	0-1	1-1	0-2	2-2	0-2	1-2	2-0	1-2	0-2	1-5	1-1	0-2
Chesterfield	1-1	5-1	1-1	1-0	0-2	0-1	1-3	1-1		1-1	0-0	2-1	0-1	2-1	1-1	2-2	2-4	1-2	3-1	2-1	3-0	1-0	2-2	0-1
Dagenham & Redbridge	0-0	3-1	2-0	0-1	3-0	3-1	1-3	6-0	3-0		0-1	1-2	2-0	4-0	0-3	2-1	2-1	0-2	6-1	1-1	3-2	1-1	1-2	0-1
Darlington	3-0	2-0	2-2	2-1	2-1	1-3	2-2	1-2	0-0	3-0		1-1	1-2	1-0	2-0	5-1	1-2	0-0	1-0	2-1	1-2	1-0	1-1	1-2
Exeter City	2-1	3-2	2-1	1-3	1-0	0-2	0-0	2-0	1-6	2-1	2-0		3-0	0-0	2-1	0-1	4-0	2-2	2-2	1-0	4-1	1-1	0-1	1-0
Gillingham	1-0	4-4	0-2	1-0	0-2	1-1	0-0	2-0	2-1	2-1	1-0	1-0		3-0	1-2	0-1	3-1	5-0	2-2	1-0	1-1	4-0	2-2	1-1
Grimsby Town	0-1	1-0	0-1	3-3	1-3	0-1	1-2	1-3	0-1	1-1	1-2	2-2	3-0		5-1	2-2	0-0	2-3	0-1	3-0	0-0	3-0	1-0	1-1
Lincoln City	5-1	0-2	2-0	3-3	0-0	2-2	1-1	1-1	3-1	1-3	0-1	0-1	2-0	1-1		0-0	1-0	1-1	1-1	0-1	1-1	0-1	0-0	1-0
Luton Town	1-2	3-1	3-1	3-3	3-3	0-1	1-2	1-1	0-0	2-1	1-2	1-2	0-0	2-1	3-2		1-0	1-1	1-1	1-3	1-1	2-4	3-1	0-1
Macclesfield Town	0-2	4-2	2-1	0-2	0-2	2-0	1-1	3-1	1-1	0-4	0-6	1-4	0-1	1-0	1-2	2-1		0-1	1-1	0-2	0-1	1-2	3-0	0-0
Morecambe	1-1	2-0	2-1	0-4	2-1	2-0	0-0	3-1	2-2	1-2	1-0	1-1	0-1	1-1	1-1	1-2	4-1		1-0	1-1	1-1	1-3	1-0	0-0
Notts County	1-1	2-1	2-0	1-1	3-1	1-1	0-1	1-2	0-1	0-3	0-0	2-1	0-1	0-2	0-1	0-2	1-1	1-0		4-2	1-2	0-3	2-2	0-2
Port Vale	0-2	0-0	0-0	3-1	0-2	0-3	1-1	3-0	0-1	0-1	3-1	1-3	1-3	2-1	0-1	1-3	1-4	2-1	1-2		2-1	0-0	1-1	1-1
Rochdale	3-1	3-1	3-1	1-1	3-0	1-2	1-1	6-1	2-1	0-2	0-2	2-2	0-1	2-0	2-2	2-0	1-1	1-1	3-0	1-0		1-2	2-1	0-1
Rotherham United	0-0	1-2	3-4	1-0	0-2	0-0	1-1	3-1	3-0	1-1	0-1	0-1	2-0	4-1	1-0	1-0	2-0	3-2	2-1	1-0	2-2		1-2	0-0
Shrewsbury Town	2-0	1-0	2-2	4-1	2-0	1-3	1-0	1-0	2-1	2-1	1-0	1-1	7-0	1-1	0-0	3-0	4-0	0-0	3-2	1-2	1-1	1-0		0-1
Wycombe Wanderers	2-1	3-0	1-1	3-1	1-0	0-0	2-1	2-0	1-1	2-1	1-1	1-1	1-0	0-1	1-0	0-0	4-0	1-1	1-2	4-2	0-1	0-0	1-1	

F.A. Premier League

Season 2008/2009

Manchester United	38	28	6	4	68	24	90
Liverpool	38	25	11	2	77	27	86
Chelsea	38	25	8	5	68	24	83
Arsenal	38	20	12	6	68	37	72
Everton	38	17	12	9	55	37	63
Aston Villa	38	17	11	10	54	48	62
Fulham	38	14	11	13	39	34	53
Tottenham Hotspur	38	14	9	15	45	45	51
West Ham United	38	14	9	15	42	45	51
Manchester City	38	15	5	18	58	50	50
Wigan Athletic	38	12	9	17	34	45	45
Stoke City	38	12	9	17	38	55	45
Bolton Wanderers	38	11	8	19	41	53	41
Portsmouth	38	10	11	17	38	57	41
Blackburn Rovers	38	10	11	17	40	60	41
Sunderland	38	9	9	20	34	54	36
Hull City	38	8	11	19	39	64	35
Newcastle United	38	7	13	18	40	59	34
Middlesbrough	38	7	11	20	28	57	32
West Bromwich Albion	38	8	8	22	36	67	32

Champions: Manchester United
Relegated: Newcastle United, Middlesbrough and West Bromwich Albion

Football League – The Championship

Season 2008/2009

Wolverhampton Wanderers	46	27	9	10	80	52	90
Birmingham City	46	23	14	9	54	37	83
Sheffield United	46	22	14	10	64	39	80
Reading	46	21	14	11	72	40	77
Burnley	46	21	13	12	72	60	76
Preston North End	46	21	11	14	66	54	74
Cardiff City	46	19	17	10	65	53	74
Swansea City	46	16	20	10	63	50	68
Ipswich Town	46	17	15	14	62	53	66
Bristol City	46	15	16	15	54	54	61
Queen's Park Rangers	46	15	16	15	42	44	61
Sheffield Wednesday	46	16	13	17	51	58	61
Watford	46	16	10	20	68	72	58
Doncaster Rovers	46	17	7	22	42	53	58
Crystal Palace	46	15	12	19	52	55	57
Blackpool	46	13	17	16	47	58	56
Coventry City	46	13	15	18	47	58	54
Derby County	46	14	12	20	55	67	54
Nottingham Forest	46	13	14	19	50	65	53
Barnsley	46	13	13	20	45	58	52
Plymouth Argyle	46	13	12	21	44	57	51
Norwich City	46	12	10	24	57	70	46
Southampton	46	10	15	21	46	69	45
Charlton Athletic	46	8	15	23	52	74	39

Promotion Play-offs

Preston North End .... 1 Sheffield United 1
Burnley .... 1 Reading 0

Sheffield United .... 1 Preston North End 0
Sheffield United won 2-1 on aggregate
Reading .... 0 Burnley 2
Burnley won 3-0 on aggregate

Burnley .... 1 Sheffield United 0

Promoted: Wolverhampton Wanderers, Birmingham City and Burnley
Relegated: Norwich City, Southampton and Charlton Athletic

Football League – League One

Season 2008/2009

Leicester City	46	27	15	4	84	39	96
Peterborough United	46	26	11	9	78	54	89
Milton Keynes Dons	46	26	9	11	83	47	87
Leeds United	46	26	6	14	77	49	84
Millwall	46	25	7	14	63	53	82
Scunthorpe United	46	22	10	14	82	63	76
Tranmere Rovers	46	21	11	14	62	49	74
Southend United	46	21	8	17	58	61	71
Huddersfield Town	46	18	14	14	62	65	68
Oldham Athletic	46	16	17	13	66	65	65
Bristol Rovers	46	17	12	17	79	61	63
Colchester United	46	18	9	19	58	58	63
Walsall	46	17	10	19	61	66	61
Leyton Orient	46	15	11	20	45	57	56
Swindon Town	46	12	17	17	68	71	53
Brighton & Hove Albion	46	13	13	20	55	70	52
Yeovil Town	46	12	15	19	41	66	51
Stockport County	46	16	12	18	59	57	50
Hartlepool United	46	13	11	22	66	79	50
Carlisle United	46	12	14	20	56	69	50
Northampton Town	46	12	13	21	61	65	49
Crewe Alexandra	46	12	10	24	59	82	46
Cheltenham Town	46	9	12	25	51	91	39
Hereford United	46	9	7	30	42	79	34

Stockport County had 10 points deducted.

Promotion Play-offs

Millwall .... 1 Leeds United 0
Scunthorpe United .... 1 Milton Keynes Dons 1

Leeds United .... 1 Millwall 1
Millwall won 2-1 on aggregate
Milton Keynes Dons .... 0 Scunthorpe United .... 0 (aet)
Aggregate 1-1. Scunthorpe United won 7-6 on penalties

Millwall .... 2 Scunthorpe United 3

Promoted: Leicester City, Peterborough United and Scunthorpe United

Relegated: Northampton Town, Crewe Alexandra, Cheltenham Town and Hereford United

Football League – League Two

Season 2008/2009

Brentford	46	23	16	7	65	36	85
Exeter City	46	22	13	11	65	50	79
Wycombe Wanderers	46	20	18	8	54	33	78
Bury	46	21	15	10	63	43	78
Gillingham	46	21	12	13	58	55	75
Rochdale	46	19	13	14	70	59	70
Shrewsbury Town	46	17	18	11	61	44	69
Dagenham & Redbridge	46	19	11	16	77	53	68
Bradford City	46	18	13	15	66	55	67
Chesterfield	46	16	15	15	62	57	63
Morecambe	46	15	18	13	53	56	63
Darlington	46	20	12	14	61	44	62
Lincoln City	46	14	17	15	53	52	59
Rotherham United	46	21	12	13	60	46	58
Aldershot Town	46	14	12	20	59	80	54
Accrington Stanley	46	13	11	22	42	59	50
Barnet	46	11	15	20	56	74	48
Port Vale	46	13	9	24	44	66	48
Notts County	46	11	14	21	49	69	47
Macclesfield Town	46	13	8	25	45	77	47
AFC Bournemouth	46	17	12	17	59	51	46
Grimsby Town	46	9	14	23	51	69	41
Chester City	46	8	13	25	43	81	37
Luton Town	46	13	17	16	58	65	26

Darlington had 10 points deducted.
Rotherham United had 17 points deducted.
AFC Bournemouth had 17 points deducted.
Luton Town had 30 points deducted.

Promotion Play-offs

Shrewsbury Town .... 0 Bury 1
Rochdale .... 0 Gillingham 1

Bury .... 0 Shrewsbury Town .... 1 (aet)
Aggregate 1-1. Shrewsbury Town won 4-3 on penalties
Gillingham .... 2 Rochdale 1
Gillingham won 2-1 on aggregate

Gillingham .... 1 Shrewsbury Town 0

Promoted: Brentford, Exeter City, Wycombe Wanderers and Gillingham

Relegated: Chester City and Luton Town

F.A. Cup 2008/2009

Round 1	9th Nov 2008	AFC Hornchurch	0	Peterborough United	1	
Round 1	8th Nov 2008	AFC Telford United	2	Southend United	2	
Round 1	10th Nov 2008	AFC Wimbledon	1	Wycombe Wanderers	4	
Round 1	8th Nov 2008	Accrington Stanley (2)	0	Tranmere Rovers	0	
Round 1	8th Nov 2008	Aldershot Town	1	Rotherham United	1	
Round 1	8th Nov 2008	Alfreton Town	4	Bury Town	2	
Round 1	8th Nov 2008	Barnet	1	Rochdale	1	
Round 1	8th Nov 2008	Blyth Spartans	3	Shrewsbury Town	1	
Round 1	8th Nov 2008	Bournemouth	1	Bristol Rovers	0	
Round 1	8th Nov 2008	Brighton & Hove Albion	3	Hartlepool United	3	
Round 1	8th Nov 2008	Bury	0	Gillingham	1	
Round 1	8th Nov 2008	Carlisle United	1	Grays Athletic	1	
Round 1	8th Nov 2008	Cheltenham Town	2	Oldham Athletic	2	
Round 1	8th Nov 2008	Chester City	0	Millwall	3	
Round 1	8th Nov 2008	Chesterfield	3	Mansfield Town	1	
Round 1	8th Nov 2008	Colchester United	0	Leyton Orient	1	
Round 1	8th Nov 2008	Crewe Alexandra	1	Ebbsfleet United	0	
Round 1	8th Nov 2008	Curzon Ashton	3	Exeter City	2	
Round 1	8th Nov 2008	Darlington	0	Droylsden	0	
Round 1	8th Nov 2008	Eastbourne Borough	0	Barrow	0	
Round 1	8th Nov 2008	Eastwood Town	2	Brackley Town	1	
Round 1	8th Nov 2008	Harlow Town	0	Macclesfield Town	2	
Round 1	9th Nov 2008	Havant & Waterlooville	1	Brentford	3	
Round 1	8th Nov 2008	Hereford United	0	Dagenham & Redbridge	0	
Round 1	8th Nov 2008	Histon	1	Swindon Town	0	
Round 1	8th Nov 2008	Huddersfield Town	3	Port Vale	4	
Round 1	8th Nov 2008	Kettering Town	1	Lincoln City	1	
Round 1	8th Nov 2008	Kidderminster Harriers	1	Cambridge United	0	
Round 1	7th Nov 2008	Leeds United	1	Northampton Town	1	
Round 1	8th Nov 2008	Leicester City	3	Stevenage Borough	0	
Round 1	8th Nov 2008	Leiston	0	Fleetwood Town	0	
Round 1	8th Nov 2008	Luton Town	0	Altrincham	0	
Round 1	8th Nov 2008	Milton Keynes Dons	1	Bradford City	2	
Round 1	8th Nov 2008	Morecambe	2	Grimsby Town	1	
Round 1	8th Nov 2008	Oxford United	0	Dorchester Town	0	
Round 1	8th Nov 2008	Sutton United	0	Notts County	1	
Round 1	9th Nov 2008	Team Bath	0	Forest Green Rovers	1	
Round 1	8th Nov 2008	Torquay United	2	Evesham United	0	
Round 1	8th Nov 2008	Walsall	1	Scunthorpe United	3	
Round 1	8th Nov 2008	Yeovil Town	1	Stockport County	1	
Replay	18th Nov 2008	Altrincham	0	Luton Town	0	(aet)
		Luton Town won on penalties				
Replay	18th Nov 2008	Barrow	4	Eastbourne Borough	0	
Replay	18th Nov 2008	Dagenham & Redbridge	2	Hereford United	1	
Replay	18th Nov 2008	Dorchester Town	1	Oxford United	3	(aet)
Replay	18th Nov 2008	Droylsden	1	Darlington	0	
Replay	18th Nov 2008	Fleetwood Town	2	Leiston	0	
Replay	29th Nov 2008	Grays Athletic	0	Carlisle United	2	
Replay	18th Nov 2008	Hartlepool United	2	Brighton & Hove Albion	1	
Replay	18th Nov 2008	Lincoln City	1	Kettering Town	2	
Replay	17th Nov 2008	Northampton Town	2	Leeds United	5	
Replay	18th Nov 2008	Oldham Athletic	0	Cheltenham Town	1	
Replay	18th Nov 2008	Rochdale	3	Barnet	2	(aet)

Replay	18th Nov 2008	Rotherham United	0	Aldershot Town	3	
Replay	18th Nov 2008	Southend United	2	AFC Telford United	0	
Replay	18th Nov 2008	Stockport County	5	Yeovil Town	0	
Replay	13th Nov 2008	Tranmere Rovers	1	Accrington Stanley	0	
Round 2	28th Nov 2008	Barrow	2	Brentford	1	
Round 2	29th Nov 2008	Bournemouth	0	Blyth Spartans	0	
Round 2	29th Nov 2008	Bradford City	1	Leyton Orient	2	
Round 2	3rd Dec 2008	Carlisle United	0	Crewe Alexandra	2	
Round 2	9th Dec 2008	Chesterfield	2	Droylsden	2	
Round 2	29th Nov 2008	Eastwood Town	2	Wycombe Wanderers	0	
Round 2	29th Nov 2008	Fleetwood Town	2	Hartlepool United	3	
Round 2	29th Nov 2008	Forest Green Rovers	2	Rochdale	0	
Round 2	29th Nov 2008	Gillingham	0	Stockport County	0	
Round 2	30th Nov 2008	Histon	1	Leeds United	0	
Round 2	29th Nov 2008	Kidderminster Harriers	2	Curzon Ashton	0	
Round 2	29th Nov 2008	Leicester City	3	Dagenham & Redbridge	2	
Round 2	29th Nov 2008	Millwall	3	Aldershot Town	0	
Round 2	2nd Dec 2008	Morecambe	2	Cheltenham Town	3	
Round 2	30th Nov 2008	Notts County	1	Kettering Town	1	
Round 2	29th Nov 2008	Peterborough United	0	Tranmere Rovers	0	
Round 2	28th Nov 2008	Port Vale	1	Macclesfield Town	3	
Round 2	29th Nov 2008	Scunthorpe United	4	Alfreton Town	0	
Round 2	29th Nov 2008	Southend United	3	Luton Town	1	
Round 2	29th Nov 2008	Torquay United	2	Oxford United	0	
Replay	16th Dec 2008	Blyth Spartans	1	Bournemouth	0	
Replay	23rd Dec 2008	Droylsden	2	Chesterfield	1	
		Droylsden were disqualified after fielding an ineligible player				
Replay	10th Dec 2008	Kettering Town	2	Notts County	1	
Replay	9th Dec 2008	Stockport County	1	Gillingham	2	
Replay	9th Dec 2008	Tranmere Rovers	1	Peterborough United	2	(aet)
Round 3	3rd Jan 2009	Arsenal	3	Plymouth Argyle	1	
Round 3	13th Jan 2009	Birmingham City	0	Wolverhampton Wanderers	2	
Round 3	5th Jan 2009	Blyth Spartans	0	Blackburn Rovers	1	
Round 3	3rd Jan 2009	Cardiff City	2	Reading	0	
Round 3	3rd Jan 2009	Charlton Athletic	1	Norwich City	1	
Round 3	3rd Jan 2009	Chelsea	1	Southend United	1	
Round 3	13th Jan 2009	Cheltenham Town	0	Doncaster Rovers	0	
Round 3	3rd Jan 2009	Coventry City	2	Kidderminster Harriers	0	
Round 3	3rd Jan 2009	Forest Green Rovers	3	Derby County	4	
Round 3	4th Jan 2009	Gillingham	1	Aston Villa	2	
Round 3	3rd Jan 2009	Hartlepool United	2	Stoke City	0	
Round 3	13th Jan 2009	Histon	1	Swansea City	2	
Round 3	3rd Jan 2009	Hull City	0	Newcastle United	0	
Round 3	3rd Jan 2009	Ipswich Town	3	Chesterfield	0	
Round 3	3rd Jan 2009	Kettering Town	2	Eastwood Town	1	
Round 3	3rd Jan 2009	Leicester City	0	Crystal Palace	0	
Round 3	13th Jan 2009	Leyton Orient	1	Sheffield United	4	
Round 3	3rd Jan 2009	Macclesfield Town	0	Everton	1	
Round 3	3rd Jan 2009	Manchester City	0	Nottingham Forest	3	
Round 3	3rd Jan 2009	Middlesbrough	2	Barrow	1	
Round 3	3rd Jan 2009	Millwall	2	Crewe Alexandra	2	

Round 3	3rd Jan 2009	Portsmouth	0	Bristol City	0	
Round 3	3rd Jan 2009	Preston North End	0	Liverpool	2	
Round 3	3rd Jan 2009	Queen's Park Rangers	0	Burnley	0	
Round 3	3rd Jan 2009	Sheffield Wednesday	1	Fulham	2	
Round 3	4th Jan 2009	Southampton	0	Manchester United	3	
Round 3	3rd Jan 2009	Sunderland	2	Bolton Wanderers	1	
Round 3	3rd Jan 2009	Torquay United	1	Blackpool	0	
Round 3	2nd Jan 2009	Tottenham Hotspur	3	Wigan Athletic	1	
Round 3	3rd Jan 2009	Watford	1	Scunthorpe United	0	
Round 3	3rd Jan 2009	West Bromwich Albion	1	Peterborough United	1	
Round 3	3rd Jan 2009	West Ham United	3	Barnsley	0	
Replay	13th Jan 2009	Bristol City	0	Portsmouth	2	
Replay	13th Jan 2009	Burnley	2	Queen's Park Rangers	1	(aet)
Replay	13th Jan 2009	Crewe Alexandra	2	Millwall	3	
Replay	14th Jan 2009	Crystal Palace	2	Leicester City	1	
Replay	20th Jan 2009	Doncaster Rovers	3	Cheltenham Town	0	
Replay	14th Jan 2009	Newcastle United	0	Hull City	1	
Replay	13th Jan 2009	Norwich City	0	Charlton Athletic	1	
Replay	13th Jan 2009	Peterborough United	0	West Bromwich Albion	2	
Replay	14th Jan 2009	Southend United	1	Chelsea	4	
Round 4	25th Jan 2009	Cardiff City	0	Arsenal	0	
Round 4	24th Jan 2009	Chelsea	3	Ipswich Town	1	
Round 4	23rd Jan 2009	Derby County	1	Nottingham Forest	1	
Round 4	24th Jan 2009	Doncaster Rovers	0	Aston Villa	0	
Round 4	24th Jan 2009	Hartlepool United	0	West Ham United	2	
Round 4	24th Jan 2009	Hull City	2	Millwall	0	
Round 4	24th Jan 2009	Kettering Town	2	Fulham	4	
Round 4	25th Jan 2009	Liverpool	1	Everton	1	
Round 4	24th Jan 2009	Manchester United	2	Tottenham Hotspur	1	
Round 4	24th Jan 2009	Portsmouth	0	Swansea City	2	
Round 4	24th Jan 2009	Sheffield United	2	Charlton Athletic	1	
Round 4	24th Jan 2009	Sunderland	0	Blackburn Rovers	0	
Round 4	24th Jan 2009	Torquay United	0	Coventry City	1	
Round 4	24th Jan 2009	Watford	4	Crystal Palace	3	
Round 4	24th Jan 2009	West Bromwich Albion	2	Burnley	2	
Round 4	24th Jan 2009	Wolverhampton Wanderers	1	Middlesbrough	2	
Replay	16th Feb 2009	Arsenal	4	Cardiff City	0	
Replay	4th Feb 2009	Aston Villa	3	Doncaster Rovers	1	
Replay	4th Feb 2009	Blackburn Rovers	2	Sunderland	1	(aet)
Replay	3rd Feb 2009	Burnley	3	West Bromwich Albion	1	
Replay	4th Feb 2009	Everton	1	Liverpool	0	(aet)
Replay	4th Feb 2009	Nottingham Forest	2	Derby County	3	
Round 5	8th Mar 2009	Arsenal	3	Burnley	0	
Round 5	14th Feb 2009	Blackburn Rovers	2	Coventry City	2	
Round 5	15th Feb 2009	Derby County	1	Manchester United	4	
Round 5	15th Feb 2009	Everton	3	Aston Villa	1	
Round 5	14th Feb 2009	Sheffield United	1	Hull City	1	
Round 5	14th Feb 2009	Swansea City	1	Fulham	1	
Round 5	14th Feb 2009	Watford	1	Chelsea	3	
Round 5	14th Feb 2009	West Ham United	1	Middlesbrough	1	

Replay	24th Feb 2009	Coventry City	1	Blackburn Rovers	0	
Replay	24th Feb 2009	Fulham	2	Swansea City	1	
Replay	26th Feb 2009	Hull City	2	Sheffield United	1	
Replay	25th Feb 2009	Middlesbrough	2	West Ham United	0	
Round 6	17th Mar 2009	Arsenal	2	Hull City	1	
Round 6	7th Mar 2009	Coventry City	0	Chelsea	2	
Round 6	8th Mar 2009	Everton	2	Middlesbrough	1	
Round 6	7th Mar 2009	Fulham	0	Manchester United	4	
Semi-Final	18th Apr 2009	Chelsea	2	Arsenal	1	
Semi-Final	19th Apr 2009	Everton	0	Manchester United	0	(aet)
		Everton won on penalties				
FINAL	30th May 2009	Chelsea	2	Everton	1	

Cup Statistics provided by:

www.soccerdata.com

Football League Cup 2008/2009

Round 1	12th Aug 2008	Bournemouth	1	Cardiff City	2	
Round 1	12th Aug 2008	Brighton & Hove Albion	4	Barnet	0	
Round 1	12th Aug 2008	Bristol City	2	Peterborough United	1	
Round 1	12th Aug 2008	Bury	0	Burnley	2	
Round 1	12th Aug 2008	Charlton Athletic	0	Yeovil Town	1	
Round 1	12th Aug 2008	Chester City	2	Leeds United	5	
Round 1	12th Aug 2008	Crewe Alexandra	2	Barnsley	0	
Round 1	12th Aug 2008	Crystal Palace	2	Hereford United	1	
Round 1	12th Aug 2008	Dagenham & Redbridge	1	Reading	2	
Round 1	12th Aug 2008	Derby County	3	Lincoln City	1	(aet)
Round 1	12th Aug 2008	Exeter City	1	Southampton	3	
Round 1	12th Aug 2008	Gillingham	0	Colchester United	1	
Round 1	12th Aug 2008	Grimsby Town	2	Tranmere Rovers	0	
Round 1	12th Aug 2008	Hartlepool United	3	Scunthorpe United	0	
Round 1	12th Aug 2008	Huddersfield Town	4	Bradford City	0	
Round 1	12th Aug 2008	Ipswich Town	4	Leyton Orient	1	
Round 1	12th Aug 2008	Leicester City	1	Stockport County	0	
Round 1	12th Aug 2008	Luton Town	2	Plymouth Argyle	0	
Round 1	12th Aug 2008	Macclesfield Town	2	Blackpool	0	
Round 1	12th Aug 2008	Millwall	0	Northampton Town	1	
Round 1	12th Aug 2008	Milton Keynes Dons	1	Norwich City	0	
Round 1	12th Aug 2008	Notts County	1	Doncaster Rovers	0	(aet)
Round 1	12th Aug 2008	Preston North End	2	Chesterfield	0	
Round 1	12th Aug 2008	Rochdale	0	Oldham Athletic	0	(aet)
		Oldham Athletic won on penalties				
Round 1	12th Aug 2008	Sheffield Wednesday	2	Rotherham United	2	(aet)
		Rotherham United won on penalties				
Round 1	12th Aug 2008	Shrewsbury Town	0	Carlisle United	1	
Round 1	12th Aug 2008	Southend United	0	Cheltenham Town	1	(aet)
Round 1	12th Aug 2008	Swansea City	2	Brentford	0	
Round 1	12th Aug 2008	Swindon Town	2	Queen's Park Rangers	3	
Round 1	12th Aug 2008	Walsall	1	Darlington	2	
Round 1	12th Aug 2008	Watford	1	Bristol Rovers	0	
Round 1	12th Aug 2008	Wolverhampton Wanderers	3	Accrington Stanley	2	
Round 1	13th Aug 2008	Coventry City	3	Aldershot	1	
Round 1	13th Aug 2008	Nottingham Forest	4	Morecambe	0	
Round 1	13th Aug 2008	Sheffield United	3	Port Vale	1	
Round 1	13th Aug 2008	Wycombe Wanderers	0	Birmingham City	4	
Round 2	26th Aug 2008	Bolton Wanderers	1	Northampton Town	2	
Round 2	26th Aug 2008	Burnley	3	Oldham Athletic	0	
Round 2	26th Aug 2008	Cardiff City	2	Milton Keynes Dons	1	
Round 2	26th Aug 2008	Cheltenham Town	2	Stoke City	3	
Round 2	26th Aug 2008	Coventry City	2	Newcastle United	3	(aet)
Round 2	26th Aug 2008	Crewe Alexandra	2	Bristol City	1	
Round 2	26th Aug 2008	Hartlepool United	3	West Bromwich Albion	1	(aet)
Round 2	26th Aug 2008	Ipswich Town	2	Colchester United	1	
Round 2	26th Aug 2008	Leeds United	4	Crystal Palace	0	
Round 2	26th Aug 2008	Middlesbrough	5	Yeovil Town	1	
Round 2	26th Aug 2008	Preston North End	0	Derby County	1	
Round 2	26th Aug 2008	Queen's Park Rangers	4	Carlisle United	0	
Round 2	26th Aug 2008	Reading	5	Luton Town	1	
Round 2	26th Aug 2008	Rotherham United	0	Wolverhampton Wanderers	0	(aet)
		Rotherham United won on penalties				
Round 2	26th Aug 2008	Southampton	2	Birmingham City	0	
Round 2	26th Aug 2008	Swansea City	2	Hull City	1	(aet)

Round 2	26th Aug 2008	Watford	2	Darlington	1	(aet)
Round 2	26th Aug 2008	Wigan Athletic	4	Notts County	0	
Round 2	27th Aug 2008	Blackburn Rovers	4	Grimsby Town	1	
Round 2	27th Aug 2008	Fulham	3	Leicester City	2	
Round 2	27th Aug 2008	Huddersfield Town	1	Sheffield United	2	
Round 2	27th Aug 2008	Nottingham Forest	1	Sunderland	2	(aet)
Round 2	27th Aug 2008	West Ham United	4	Macclesfield Town	1	(aet)
Round 2	24th Sep 2008	Brighton & Hove Albion	2	Manchester City	2	(aet)
		Brighton & Hove Albion won on penalties				
Round 3	23rd Sep 2008	Arsenal	6	Sheffield United	0	
Round 3	23rd Sep 2008	Burnley	1	Fulham	0	
Round 3	23rd Sep 2008	Leeds United	3	Hartlepool United	2	
Round 3	23rd Sep 2008	Liverpool	2	Crewe Alexandra	1	
Round 3	23rd Sep 2008	Manchester United	3	Middlesbrough	1	
Round 3	23rd Sep 2008	Rotherham United	3	Southampton	1	
Round 3	23rd Sep 2008	Stoke City	2	Reading	2	(aet)
		Stoke City won on penalties				
Round 3	23rd Sep 2008	Sunderland	2	Northampton Town	2	(aet)
		Sunderland won on penalties				
Round 3	23rd Sep 2008	Swansea City	1	Cardiff City	0	
Round 3	23rd Sep 2008	Watford	1	West Ham United	0	
Round 3	24th Sep 2008	Aston Villa	0	Queen's Park Rangers	1	
Round 3	24th Sep 2008	Blackburn Rovers	1	Everton	0	
Round 3	24th Sep 2008	Ipswich Town	1	Wigan Athletic	4	
Round 3	24th Sep 2008	Newcastle United	1	Tottenham Hotspur	2	
Round 3	24th Sep 2008	Portsmouth	0	Chelsea	4	
Round 3	4th Nov 2008	Brighton & Hove Albion	1	Derby County	4	
Round 4	11th Nov 2008	Arsenal	3	Wigan Athletic	0	
Round 4	11th Nov 2008	Derby County	2	Leeds United	1	
Round 4	11th Nov 2008	Manchester United	1	Queen's Park Rangers	0	
Round 4	11th Nov 2008	Stoke City	2	Rotherham United	0	
Round 4	11th Nov 2008	Swansea City	0	Watford	1	
Round 4	12th Nov 2008	Chelsea	1	Burnley	1	(aet)
		Burnley won on penalties				
Round 4	12th Nov 2008	Sunderland	1	Blackburn Rovers	2	
Round 4	12th Nov 2008	Tottenham Hotspur	4	Liverpool	2	
Round 5	2nd Dec 2008	Burnley	2	Arsenal	0	
Round 5	2nd Dec 2008	Stoke City	0	Derby County	1	
Round 5	3rd Dec 2008	Manchester United	5	Blackburn Rovers	3	
Round 5	3rd Dec 2008	Watford	1	Tottenham Hotspur	2	
Semi-finals						
1st leg	7th Jan 2009	Derby County	1	Manchester United	0	
2nd leg	20th Jan 2009	Manchester United	4	Derby County	2	
		Manchester United won 4-3 on aggregate				
1st leg	6th Jan 2009	Tottenham Hotspur	4	Burnley	1	
2nd leg	21st Jan 2009	Burnley	3	Tottenham Hotspur	2	(aet)
		Tottenham Hotspur won 6-4 on aggregate				
FINAL	1st Mar 2009	Manchester United	0	Tottenham Hotspur	0	(aet)
		Manchester United won on penalties				

ENGLAND INTERNATIONAL LINE-UPS AND STATISTICS 2008

6th February 2008
v SWITZERLAND *Wembley*

D. James	Portsmouth
W. Brown	Manchester United
R. Ferdinand	Manchester United
M. Upson	West Ham United
A. Cole	Chelsea (sub. W. Bridge 73)
D. Bentley	Blackburn Rovers
J. Jenas	Tottenham H. (sub. Wright-Phillips 57)
S. Gerrard	Liverpool
G. Barry	Aston Villa (sub. O. Hargreaves 74)
J. Cole	Chelsea (sub. P. Crouch 58)
W. Rooney	Manchester Utd. (sub. A. Young 87)

Result 2-1 Jenas, Wright-Phillips

26th March 2008
v FRANCE *Paris*

D. James	Portsmouth
W. Brown	Manchester U. (sub. G. Johnson 64)
R. Ferdinand	Manchester United
J. Terry	Chelsea (sub. J. Lescott 46)
A. Cole	Chelsea
D. Beckham	L.A. Galaxy (sub. D. Bentley 63)
O. Hargreaves	Manchester United
G. Barry	Aston Villa
J. Cole	Chelsea (sub. J. Lescott 46)
S. Gerrard	Liverpool (sub. M. Owen 47)
W. Rooney	Manchester Utd. (sub. P. Crouch 47)

Result 0-1

28th May 2008
v U.S.A. *Wembley*

D. James	Portsmouth
W. Brown	Manchester Utd (sub. G. Johnson 57)
R. Ferdinand	Manchester United
J. Terry	Chelsea
A. Cole	Chelsea (sub. W. Bridge 82)
D. Beckham	L.A. Galaxy (sub. D. Bentley 46)
O. Hargreaves	Manchester United
F. Lampard	Chelsea (sub. G. Barry 58)
S. Gerrard	Liverpool
J. Defoe	Portsmouth (sub. P. Crouch 68)
W. Rooney	Manchester United (sub. J. Cole 78)

Result 2-0 Terry, Gerrard

1st June 2008
v TRINIDAD & TOBAGO
Port-of-Spain

D. James	Portsmouth (sub. J. Hart 45)
R. Ferdinand	Manchester Utd. (sub. P. Jagielka 46)
D. Beckham	L.A. Galaxy (sub. D. Bentley 46)
G. Johnson	Portsmouth
J. Woodgate	Tottenham Hotspur
W. Bridge	Chelsea (sub. S. Warnock 84)
G. Barry	Aston Villa
S. Gerrard	Liverpool
S. Downing	Middlesbrough (sub. Young 57)
D. Ashton	West Ham United (sub. P. Crouch 47)
J. Defoe	Portsmouth (sub. T. Walcott 69)

Result 3-0 Barry, Defoe 2

20th August 2008
v CZECH REPUBLIC *Wembley*

D. James	Portsmouth
R. Ferdinand	Man. United (sub. J. Woodgate 57)
A. Cole	Chelsea
W. Brown	Manchester United
J. Terry	Chelsea
S. Gerrard	Liverpool (sub. J. Cole 57)
G. Barry	Aston Villa
D. Beckham	L.A. Galaxy (sub. J. Jenas 79)
F. Lampard	Chelsea (sub. D. Bentley 79)
J. Defoe	Portsmouth (sub. E. Heskey 46)
W. Rooney	Man. United (sub. S. Downing 69)

Result 2-2 Brown, J. Cole

6th September 2008
v ANDORRA (WCQ) *Barcelona*

D. James	Portsmouth
J. Lescott	Everton
A. Cole	Chelsea
J. Terry	Chelsea
G. Johnson	Portsmouth
G. Barry	Aston Villa
F. Lampard	Chelsea (sub. D. Beckham 79)
S. Downing	Middlesbrough (sub. J. Cole 46)
J. Defoe	Portsmouth (sub. E. Heskey 46)
W. Rooney	Manchester United
T. Walcott	Arsenal

Result 2-0 J. Cole 2

ENGLAND INTERNATIONAL LINE-UPS AND STATISTICS 2008-2009

11th September 2008

v CROATIA (WCQ) *Zagreb*

D. James	Portsmouth
R. Ferdinand	Manchester United
A. Cole	Chelsea
W. Brown	Manchester United
J. Terry	Chelsea (sub. M. Upson 88)
J. Cole	Chelsea (sub. J. Jenas 55)
G. Barry	Aston Villa
F. Lampard	Chelsea
E. Heskey	Wigan Athletic
W. Rooney	Manchester United
T. Walcott	Arsenal (sub. D. Beckham 84)

Result 4-1 Walcott 3, Rooney

11th October 2008

v KAZAKHSTAN (WCQ) *Wembley*

D. James	Portsmouth
R. Ferdinand	Manchester United
M. Upson	West Ham United
A. Cole	Chelsea
W. Brown	Manchester United
S. Gerrard	Liverpool
G. Barry	Aston V. (sub. S. Wright-Phillips 46)
F. Lampard	Chelsea
E. Heskey	Wigan Athletic
W. Rooney	Manchester United (sub. J. Defoe 86)
T. Walcott	Arsenal (sub. D. Beckham 79)

Result 5-1 Ferdinand, Kuchma (og), Rooney 2, Defoe

15th October 2008

v BELARUS (WCQ) *Minsk*

D. James	Portsmouth
R. Ferdinand	Manchester United
W. Bridge	Chelsea
M. Upson	West Ham United
W. Brown	Manchester United
S. Gerrard	Liverpool
G. Barry	Aston Villa
F. Lampard	Chelsea
E. Heskey	Wigan Athletic (sub. P. Crouch 70)
W. Rooney	Man. United (sub. D. Beckham 87)
T. Walcott	Arsenal (sub. S. Wright-Phillips 68)

Result 3-1 Gerrard, Rooney 2

19th November 2008

v GERMANY *Berlin*

D. James	Portsmouth (sub. S. Carson 46)
M. Upson	West Ham United
J. Terry	Chelsea
W. Bridge	Chelsea
G. Johnson	Portsmouth
G. Barry	Aston Villa
M. Carrick	Manchester United
S. Downing	Middlesbrough
S. Wright-Phillips	Manchester City (sub. P. Crouch 90)
J. Defoe	Portsmouth (sub. D. Bent 46)
G. Agbonlahor	Aston Villa (sub. A. Young 77)

Result 2-1 Upson, Terry

11th February 2009

v SPAIN *Seville*

D. James	Portsmouth (sub. R. Green 46)
J. Terry	Chelsea
P. Jagielka	Everton (sub. M. Upson 46)
A. Cole	Chelsea
G. Johnson	Portsmouth
G. Barry	Aston Villa (sub. F. Lampard 46)
M. Carrick	Manchester United
S. Downing	Middlesbrough (sub. D. Beckham 46)
S. Wright-Phillips	Manchester City
G. Agbonlahor	Aston Villa (sub. C. Cole 76)
E. Heskey	Aston Villa (sub. P. Crouch 46)

Result 0-2

28th March 2009

v SLOVAKIA *Wembley*

D. James	Portsmouth (sub. B. Foster 46)
M. Upson	West Ham United
J. Terry	Chelsea
A. Cole	Chelsea
G. Johnson	Portsmouth
G. Barry	Aston Villa
F. Lampard	Chelsea
S. Gerrard	Liverpool (sub. S. Downing 46)
A. Lennon	Tottenham H. (sub. D. Beckham 46)
W. Rooney	Manchester United
E. Heskey	Aston Villa (sub. C. Cole 15 (sub. P. Crouch 35 (sub. M. Carrick 74)))

Result 4-0 Heskey, Rooney 2, Lampard

ENGLAND INTERNATIONAL LINE-UPS AND STATISTICS 2009

1st April 2009

v UKRAINE (WCQ) *Wembley*

D. James	Portsmouth
R. Ferdinand	Man. United (sub. P. Jagielka 88)
A. Cole	Chelsea
J. Terry	Chelsea
G. Johnson	Portsmouth
S. Gerrard	Liverpool
G. Barry	Aston Villa
F. Lampard	Chelsea
A. Lennon	Tottenham H. (sub. D. Beckham 67)
P. Crouch	Portsmouth (sub. S. Wright-Phillips 79)
W. Rooney	Manchester United

Result 2-1 Crouch, Terry

6th June 2009

v KAZAKHSTAN (WCQ) *Almaty*

R. Green	West Ham United
M. Upson	West Ham United
J. Terry	Chelsea
A. Cole	Chelsea
G. Johnson	Portsmouth (sub. D. Beckham 75)
S. Gerrard	Liverpool
G. Barry	Manchester City
F. Lampard	Chelsea
T. Walcott	Arsenal (sub. S. Wright-Phillips 46)
E. Heskey	Aston Villa (sub. J. Defoe 81)
W. Rooney	Manchester United

Result 4-0 Barry, Heskey, Rooney, Lampard (pen)

10th June 2009

v ANDORRA (WCQ) *Wembley*

R. Green	West Ham United
J. Lescott	Everton
A. Cole	Chelsea (sub. W. Bridge 63)
J. Terry	Chelsea
G. Johnson	Portsmouth
S. Gerrard	Liverpool (sub. A. Young 46)
D. Beckham	L.A. Galaxy
F. Lampard	Chelsea
T. Walcott	Arsenal
P. Crouch	Portsmouth
W. Rooney	Manchester United (sub. J. Defoe 46)

Result 6-0 Rooney 2, Lampard, Defoe 2, Crouch

Supporters' Guides Series

This top-selling series has been published since 1982 and the new editions contain the 2008/2009 Season's results and tables, Directions, Photos, Phone numbers, Parking information, Admission details, Disabled info and much more.

THE SUPPORTERS' GUIDE TO PREMIER & FOOTBALL LEAGUE CLUBS 2010

This 26th edition covers all 92 Premiership and Football League clubs. ***Price £6.99***

NON-LEAGUE SUPPORTERS' GUIDE AND YEARBOOK 2010

This 18th edition covers all 68 clubs in Step 1 & Step 2 of Non-League football – the Football Conference National, Conference North and Conference South. ***Price £6.99***

THE SUPPORTERS' GUIDE TO SCOTTISH FOOTBALL 2009

The 17th edition featuring all Scottish Premier League, Scottish League and Highland League clubs. ***Price £6.99***

THE SUPPORTERS' GUIDE TO NON-LEAGUE FOOTBALL 2007 – STEP 3 CLUBS

Following the reorganisation of Non-League Football the 3rd edition of this book features the 66 clubs which feed into the Football Conference. ***Price £6.99***

THE SUPPORTERS' GUIDE TO WELSH FOOTBALL GROUNDS 2007

The 11th edition featuring all League of Wales, Cymru Alliance & Welsh Football League Clubs + results, tables & much more. ***Price £6.99***

THE SUPPORTERS' GUIDE TO NORTHERN IRISH FOOTBALL 2007

This 4th edition features all Irish Premier League and Irish Football League Clubs + results, tables & much more. ***Price £6.99***

THE SUPPORTERS' GUIDE TO EIRCOM FAI CLUBS 2006

Back after a long absence this 4th edition features all Eircom League Premier and First Division Clubs + 10 years of results, tables & much more. ***Price £6.99***

These books are available UK & Surface post free from –

Soccer Books Limited (Dept. SBL)
72 St. Peter's Avenue
Cleethorpes
N.E. Lincolnshire